Power
Puzzles

Power Puzzles

Philip Carter and Ken Russell

BARNES
&NOBLE
BOOKS
NEW YORK

Barnes & Noble, Inc. edition published by
arrangement with Robinson Publishing Ltd.

First published in the UK by Robinson Publishing Ltd. 1994

1995 Barnes & Noble Books

ISBN 1-56619-720-1

Printed and bound in the United States of America

M   9   8   7   6   5   4   3   2   1

About the Authors

Philip Carter is a Justice of the Peace and an estimator from Yorkshire. He is puzzle editor of *Enigmasig*, the monthly newsletter of the British Mensa Puzzle Special Interest group.

Ken Russell is a London surveyor and is puzzle editor of *British Mensa*, a magazine sent to its 43,000 British members monthly.

Acknowledgments

We are indebted to our wives, both named Barbara, for checking and typing the manuscript, and for their encouragement in our various projects.

About Mensa

Mensa is a social club for which membership is accepted from all persons with an IQ (Intelligence Quotient) of 148 or above on the CATTELL scale of intelligence. This represents the top 2% of the population. Therefore one person in 50 is capable of passing the entrance test, which consists of a series of intelligence tests.

Mensa is the Latin word for *table*. We are a round-table society where all persons are of equal standing. There are three aims: social contact among intelligent people; research in psychology; and the identification and fostering of intelligence.

Mensa is an international society with 110,000 members of all occupations: clerks, doctors, lawyers, policeofficers, industrial workers, teachers, nurses, and many more.

Enquiries to: MENSA FREEPOST
Wolverhampton WV2 1BR
England

MENSA INTERNATIONAL
15 The Ivories,
6-8 Northampton Street,
London N1 2HV
England

AMERICAN MENSA LTD.
2626 East 14th Street
Brooklyn, NY 11235

The
Puzzles

1 "X" Puzzle

Find twenty-two words in the grid, each must have at least one X in it. Words may be in any direction but always in a straight line.

D	I	O	L	Y	X	X
E	X	A	M	E	Y	I
X	A	L	S	L	L	P
T	I	Y	E	X	E	H
E	E	N	X	O	M	O
R	E	X	A	C	T	I
X	Y	P	T	U	X	D

(Solution 4)

2 Warehouse

A warehouse has to be built at one of the mile points along a road so that its weekly delivery miles are kept to a minimum.

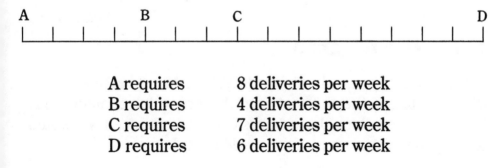

A requires	8 deliveries per week
B requires	4 deliveries per week
C requires	7 deliveries per week
D requires	6 deliveries per week

Where should the warehouse be built?

(Solution 8)

1

3 Alphabet Crossword

Complete the grid by using all twenty-six letters of the alphabet.

A B C D E F G H I J K L M
N O P Q R S T U V W X Y Z

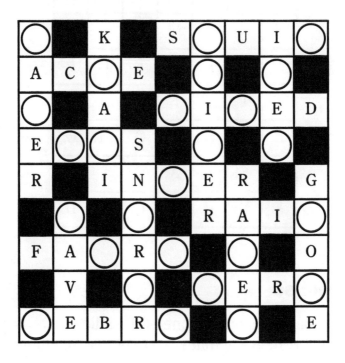

(Solution 11)

4 Reverse Anagram

If we presented you with the words MAR, AM, and FAR and asked you to find the shortest English word which contained all the letters from which these words could be produced, we would expect you to come up with the world FARM.

Here is a further list of words:

BEAT, ROUTE, BRAIN, MINT

What is the shortest English word from which all these words can be produced?

(Solution 16)

2

5 No Blanks

The blank squares have been removed from this crossword. Letters have been inserted in their place. You have to find the blank squares.

S	C	A	L	A	R	A	R	E	M	A	N	D
E	R	R	I	C	E	P	A	P	E	R	E	I
M	I	T	T	E	N	A	M	E	T	R	E	S
I	O	I	O	R	E	V	U	E	O	I	D	I
C	A	S	T	A	W	A	S	L	O	V	E	N
O	L	T	E	G	A	T	E	H	O	E	D	V
N	O	O	N	E	W	I	F	E	Z	S	R	E
D	O	C	O	T	E	M	I	N	E	T	I	S
U	P	O	N	P	L	A	C	E	S	O	F	T
C	A	V	E	D	O	N	O	R	T	I	T	M
T	R	E	P	A	N	O	M	E	A	L	I	E
O	E	R	E	M	E	D	I	A	T	E	E	N
R	O	T	T	E	R	O	C	R	E	D	I	T

(Solution 21)

6 Fair Play

In a game of thirty-six players that lasts just fifteen minutes, there are four reserve players. The reserves alternate equally with each player, therefore, all forty players are on the sportsfield for the same length of time. For how long?

(Solution 23)

7 Anagrammed Synonyms

In each of the following, study the list of three words. Your task is to find two of the three words which can be paired to form an anagram of one word which is a synonym of the word remaining. For example:

LEG - MEEK - NET

The words LEG and NET are an anagram of GENTLE, which is a synonym of the word remaining, MEEK.

1. BIDS - SEE - TOO
2. VEERED - WEAK - TAN
3. SIT - HIND - POORER
4. OUT - KISS - SCALE
5. POST - SLAP - AIDE
6. TREE - ART - EBB
7. WHET - MUTE - TAILS
8. DRAIN - ONCE - ACT
9. SIN - EAT - GET
10. SANE - VICE - SKEW

(Solution 27)

8 1984

The digits 0, 1, 2, 3, 4, 5, 6, 7, 8, 9 can be arranged into an addition sum to add up to almost any total, except that nobody has yet found a way to add up to 1984.

However, nine digits can equal 1984 by an addition sum. Which digit is omitted?

(Solution 32)

4

9   Round the Hexagons

Can you work out what should be the contents of the bottom hexagon?

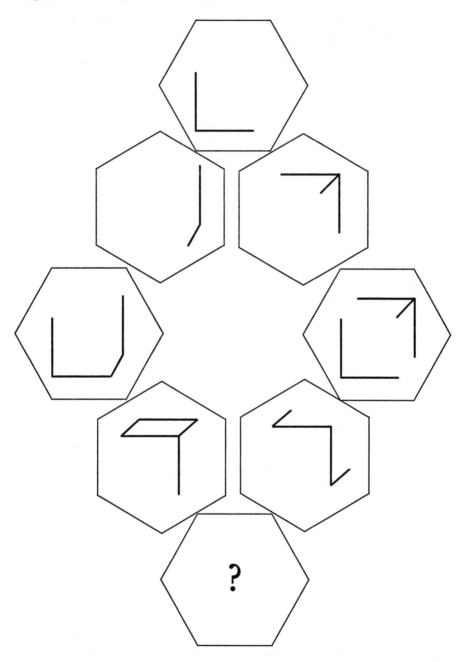

(Solution 36)

10 Hexagon

Fit the following words into the six spaces encircling the appropriate number on the diagram so that each word correctly interlinks with the two words on either side (you will see that each word has two consecutive letters in common with the word on its side). (NOTE: To arrive at the correct solution some words will have to be entered clockwise and some counter-clockwise.)

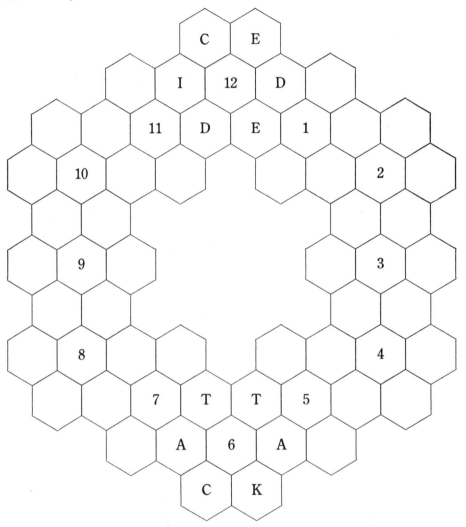

ADROIT – DEFERS – GERUND – ROTATE – REMARK – TAGGED – ~~ATTACK~~ – ~~DECIDE~~ – URGENT – MALADY – WIDENS – DIVIDE

(Solution 40)

11 Circles

Which of these fit into the blank circle to carry on a logical sequence?

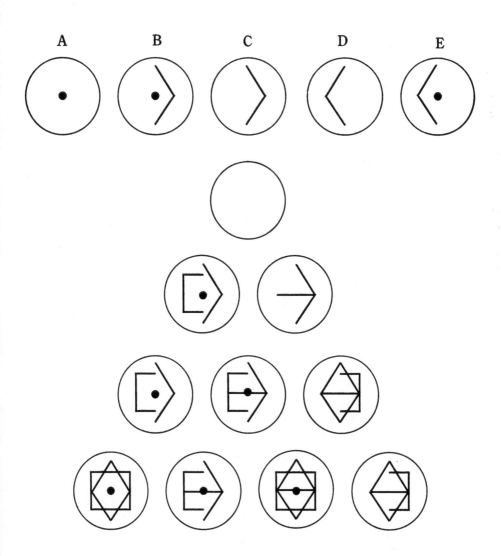

(Solution 44)

12 Target Crossword

Find sixteen 6-letter words by pairing up the thirty-two 3-letter bits.

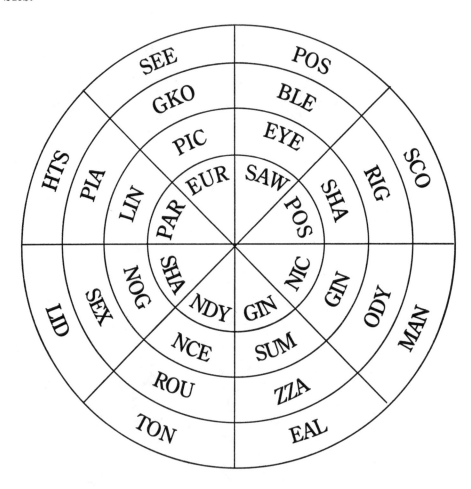

(Solution 50)

13 Sequence

What number comes next in this sequence?

101, 65, 131, 116, 131, 1021, ?

(Solution 54)

14 No Repeat Letters

The grid below contains twenty-five different letters of the alphabet. What is the longest word which can be found by starting anywhere and working from square to square horizontally, vertically, or diagonally, and not repeating a letter?

J	N	B	D	I
X	E	R	V	G
P	O	C	U	Q
S	K	T	W	L
Y	H	M	A	F

(Solution 58)

15 Word Circle

Complete the fifteen words below so that two letters are common to each word. That is, reading across, the same two letters that end the first word also start the second word, and the two letters which end the second also start the third word, etc. The two letters that end the fifteenth word also are the first two letters of the first word, to complete the circle.

..AR..	..EE..	..NA..	..NU..
..SU..	..TT..	..GA..	..PH..
..MI..	..BU..	..VI..	..EL..
..ND..	..IG..	..FE..	

(Solution 61)

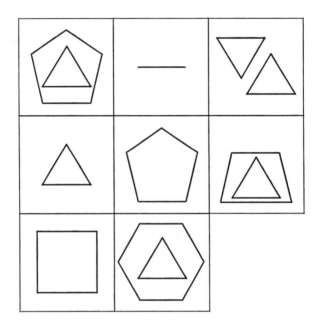

Which of the following is the missing square?

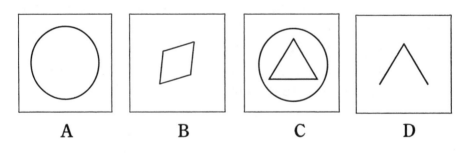

A   B   C   D

(Solution 66)

17 Logic

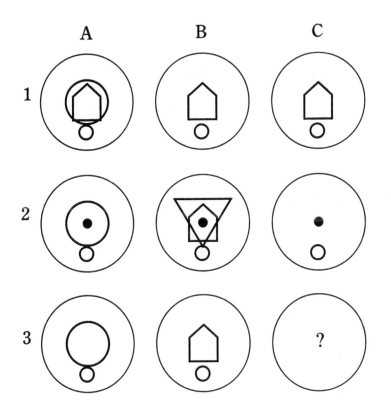

Logically which circle below fits the above pattern?

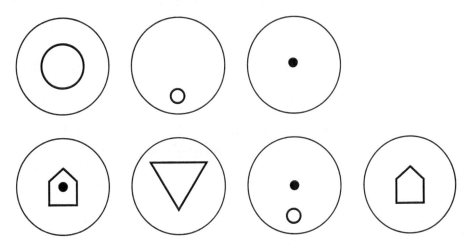

(Solution 70)

18 Sequence

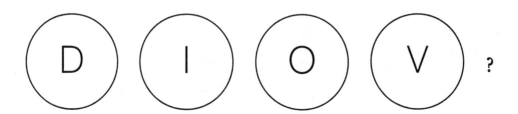

Which option carries on the sequence?

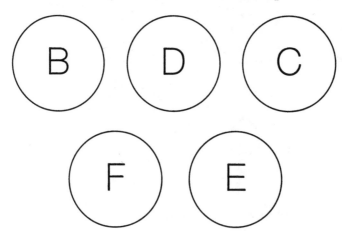

(Solution 79)

19 Old Age

In ten years time the combined age of two brothers and two
sisters will be 100. What will it be in seven years time?

(Solution 74)

20 Word Search

Find twenty words to do with D R I N K S.

Words run backward, forward, vertically, horizontally, and
diagonally, but always in a straight line.

E	S	U	E	R	T	R	A	H	C
N	E	Y	V	E	Z	L	O	A	O
I	R	N	A	Z	C	C	P	X	I
D	E	W	I	O	K	P	K	N	N
A	G	F	H	D	U	C	I	A	T
N	A	O	G	C	A	T	H	E	R
E	L	O	C	R	R	C	L	O	E
R	R	I	R	A	G	M	S	E	A
G	N	A	M	O	I	E	L	U	U
O	R	A	N	G	E	A	D	E	M

(Solution 83)

21 Letters Sequence

Which two letters come next in the following sequence?
                TO, NE, US, RN, ER, RS, ?

(Solution 87)

13

22 Bracket Word

Place two letters in each bracket so that these finish the word on the left and start the word on the right. The letters in the brackets, read downwards in pairs, will spell out a 10-letter word.

ME (..) AS

UN (..) UT

S A (..) NE

MO (..) I N

L E (..) GO

(Solution 91)

23 Odd One Out

Which is the odd one out?

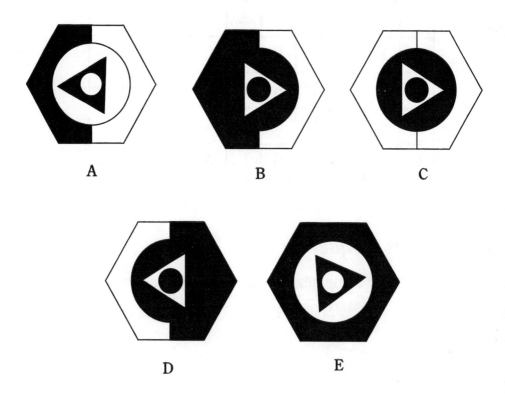

(Solution 95)

24 Word Power

In column (A) is a list of words. The problem is to rearrange them so that their initial letters spell out a quotation. To make the task easier, refer to the definition in column (B) and put the correct word with that definition in the answer column (C). When all the words have been correctly placed in column (C), the quotation will then appear reading down the initial letters.

(A) Words	(B) Definitions	(C) Answers
KOHL	Unearthly, weird	————
ESCULENT	A rare word for edict	————
TOLU	Refreshment with food and drink	————
GERUND	Uproot	————
ELDRICH	A cosmetic powder	————
VICARIOUS	With great strength	————
UKASE	Penniless	————
INANITION	Delegated	————
AMAIN	Edible	————
ODALISK	A noun formed from a verb ending -ing	————
REFECTION	Female slave in a harem	————
IMPECUNIOUS	A female swan	————
EXTIRPATE	Exhaustion	————
TERMAGANT	An aromatic balsam	————

(Solution 99)

25 Greek Cross to Square Puzzle

Draw two lines which will dissect the Greek Cross into four congruent (same size and shape) pieces which can then be arranged to form a square.

(Solution 103)

26 Appropriate Anagrams

Find the appropriate anagrams of these words and phrases.

PARADISE REGAINED

SAINT ELMO'S FIRE

SAUCINESS

SEMOLINA

TOTAL ABSTAINERS

WAITRESS

THERAPEUTICS

THE MONA LISA

MEDICAL CONSULTATIONS

A SENTENCE OF DEATH

(Solution 107)

27 Jumble

Beginning always with the middle letter "V," spell out eight 11-letter words traveling in any direction. Each letter (except for the "V") can only be used once.

I	T	Y	E	R	I	S	L	Y
L	C	U	T	A	O	U	Y	L
I	I	L	A	C	X	A	U	S
T	M	R	E	I	E	T	I	O
P	A	S	E	**V**	A	C	I	A
I	H	R	I	E	E	C	N	T
Y	S	C	E	R	N	N	T	I
O	E	O	S	U	T	A	I	O
R	E	M	N	O	I	T	L	N

(Solution 111)

28 Four Integers

ABCD represents four integers such that the following arrangements are square numbers. What integer does each letter represent?

CABA
DCBA
DACB

(Solution 114)

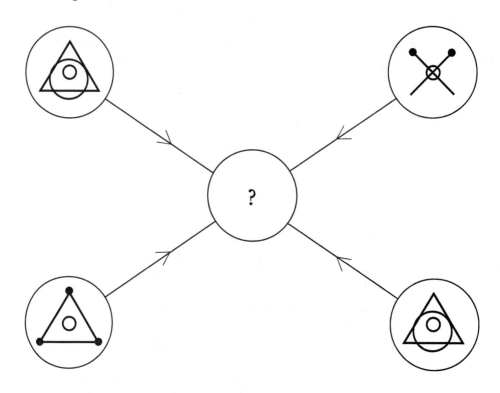

Each line and symbol which appears in the four outer circles is transferred to the center circle according to these rules:

If a line or symbol occurs in the outer circles:

once	it is transferred
twice	it is possibly transferred
three times	it is transferred
four times	it is not transferred

Which of the circles A, B, C, D, or E, shown opposite, should appear at the center of the diagram?

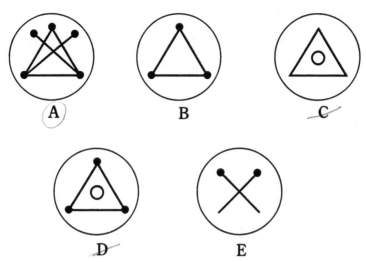

(Solution 116)

30 Cheeses

Six cheeses of different sizes are placed on stool A. How many moves will it take to move the cheeses one by one to stool C? A cheese must not be placed on a cheese smaller than itself.

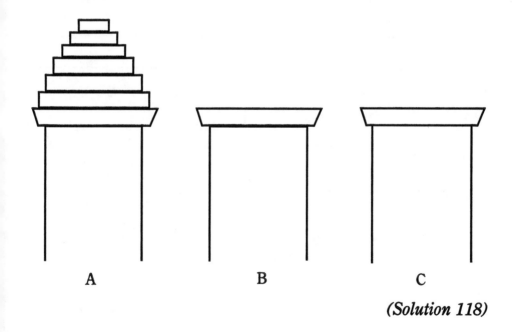

A   B   C

(Solution 118)

31 The Gallopers

The name given to this puzzle is the old fairground name for the roundabout ride on horses, now more familiarly known as the carousel.

Complete the words in each column, all of which end in G. The scrambled letters in the section to the right of each column are an anagram of a word which will give you a clue to the word you are trying to find, to put in the column.

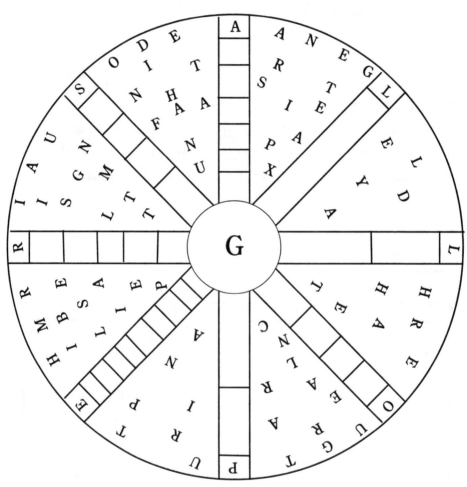

(Solution 124)

32 Analogy

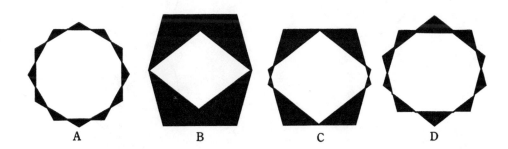

A   B   C   D

(Solution 129)

33 Birds

The twenty-five words can be paired up to make twelve birds with one word left over. Which is the word?

GREBE	WARBLER	DOVE	WATER	PIGEON
CARRIER	PEACOCK	HAWK	PETREL	SNOW
NIGHT	MUSCOVY	WILLOW	BLACK	OUSEL
COCKATOO	HOUSE	GOOSE	OWL	MARTIN
STORMY	DUCK	TAWNY	TURTLE	CRESTED

(Solution 133)

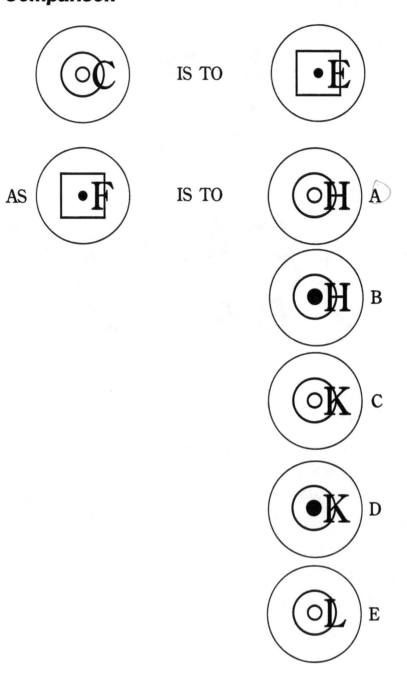

IS TO

AS

IS TO

(Solution 121)

35 Knight

Using the knight's move as in chess, spell out the message. You have to find the starting point.

AS	IT	OWN	PEOPLE'S	ARE
BUT	OTHER	ARE	HARD	OUR
FIND	SILLY	BELIEVE	PROBABLY	THOUGHTS
THAT	THEY	WE	AS	TO

	x		x	
x				x
		Knight		
x				x
	x		x	

(Solution 135)

23

36 Series

Write down the tenth term of

$$6, 18, 54, \ldots$$

And find a formula for quickly working out the answer.

(Solution 138)

$6 \cdot 3^{n-1}$

37 Division

Divide the grid into four equal parts, each of which should be the same shape and contain the same nine letters which can be arranged into a 9-letter word.

N	T	G	E	O	O
N	U	Y	N	S	S
Y	U	R	R	Y	E
R	G	O	S	U	G
E	Y	S	O	T	U
T	G	E	T	R	N

(Solution 142)

38 Three Animals

Use all the letters in the sentence below only once to spell out the names of three animals.

ALL HERE NAME A POT PLANT

(Solution 146)

39 Equilateral Triangle

Draw in the largest possible equilateral triangle so that it does not touch another triangle and does not overlap the sides of the grid.

(Solution 151)

40 Directional Numbers

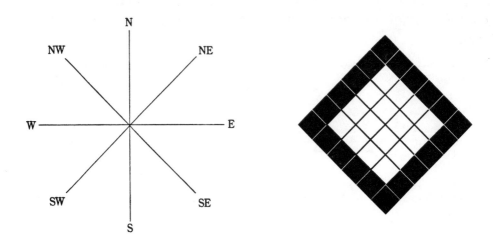

Fit all the numbers below into the grid. Each number must travel in a straight line in the direction of a compass point and start and finish in a shaded square.

217932	28778	6884	632
482912	34981		984
834252			
911763			
864131			
882122			
982711			
276966			
417644			
924492			

(Solution 157)

41 Find a Word

Trace out a 13-letter word by moving along the lines. You need to find the starting letter and must not cross a letter twice.

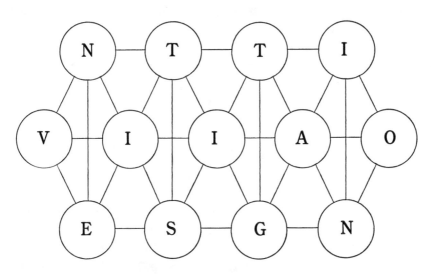

(Solution 1)

42 Synonym Circles

Read clockwise to find two 8-letter words which are synonyms. You have to find the starting point and provide the missing letters.

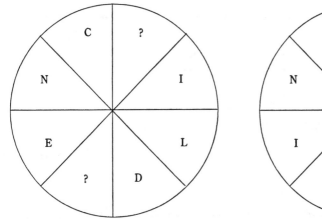
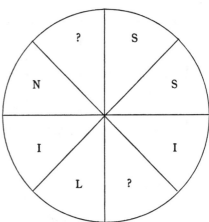

(Solution 5)

43 Grid

Each of the nine squares 1A to 3C should incorporate all the lines and symbols which are shown in the outer squares A, B, or C and 1, 2, or 3. Thus 2B should incorporate all the lines and symbols in 2 and B.

One of the squares, 1A to 3C, is incorrect. Which one is it?

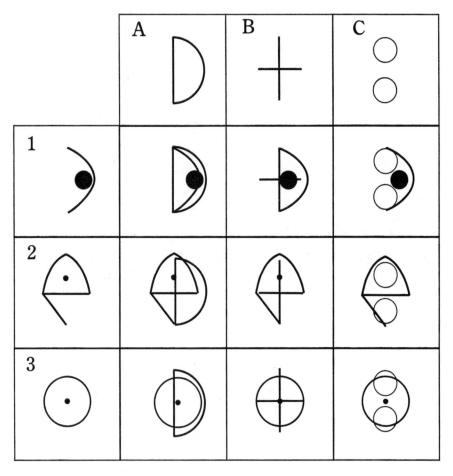

(Solution 9)

44 Chairs

In how many ways may eight people sit on eight chairs arranged in a line, if two of them insist on sitting next to each other?

(Solution 13)

28

45 Double-Bigrams

A bigram is any sequence of two consecutive letters in a word, for instance IG in the word BIGRAM, and a double-bigram is such a sequence which occurs twice in succession, such as IGIG in the word WHIRLIGIG.

Below we list several double-bigrams. Can you complete the words in which they occur?

••• POPO ••••••
••• LOLO ••
••• ENEN •••
••• VIVI ••
•• LALA •••
•• TITI ••
•• BIBI ••
••• WAWA •
•• OTOT •••
•• ODOD •••••••
• NINI •••••••
••• ININ •
••• DIDI ••
• ATAT ••••

(Solution 17)

46 Number

What number is missing from the grid?

8	12	6
3	20	6
3	9	?

(Solution 20)

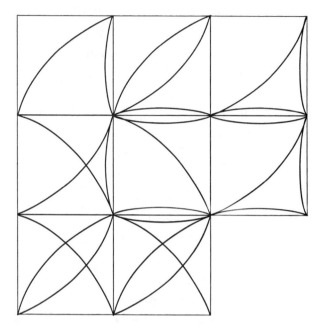

Look across each horizontal line of boxes and down each vertical line of boxes and choose the missing square from the options below.

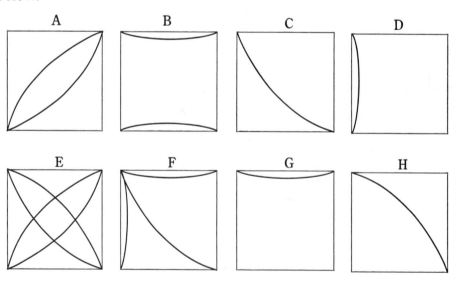

(Solution 25)

48 Anagrammed Magic Square

Using all twenty-five letters of the sentence below only once, form five 5-letter words which when placed correctly in the grid will form a magic word square where the same five words can be read both horizontally and vertically.

CARTER'S NORTHERN FACE SAFEST

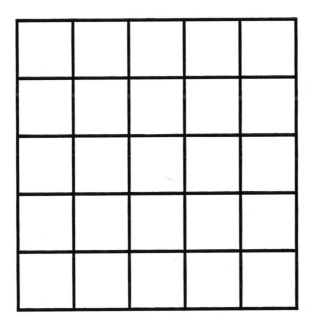

(Solution 29)

49 Stations

There are eight stations from town A to town B. How many different single tickets must be printed so that one may book from any station to any other?

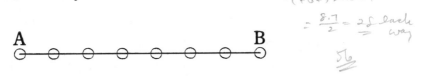

$7 + 6 + 5 + \ldots + 1$

$= \frac{8 \cdot 7}{2} = 28 \text{ each way}$

56

(Solution 33)

50 Hexagram

Solve the six anagrams of FISH. Transfer the six arrowed letters to the key box and solve this anagram to discover a key seventh.

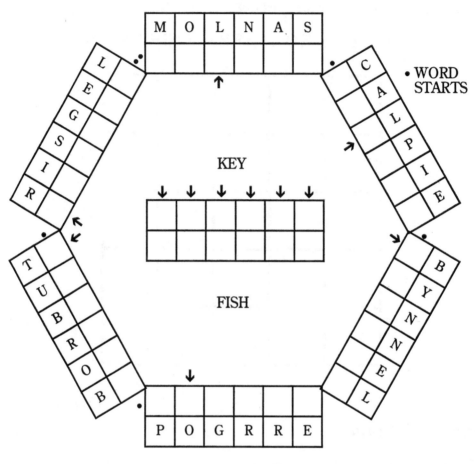

(Solution 37)

51 Homonym

A homonym is a word having the same sound and perhaps the same spelling as another, but differing in meaning. For example, Cleave and Cleave or Sun and Son. The words I and Eye are examples of a pair of homonyms in which none of the letters in one word appear in the other. Can you find another pair of homonyms which have this feature?

(Solution 41)

52 Circles

Which of these fit into the blank circle to carry on a logical sequence?

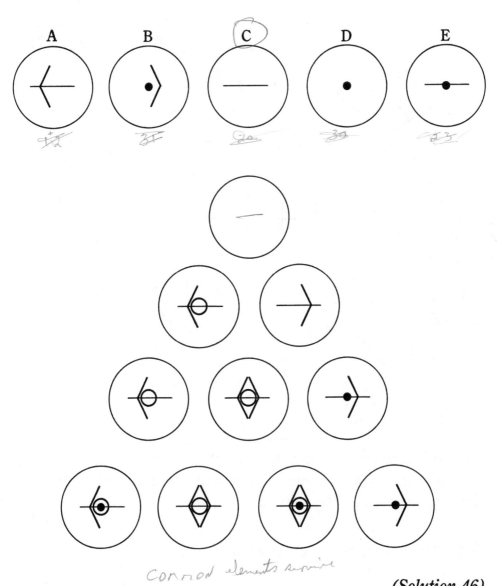

(Solution 46)

53 Pentagram

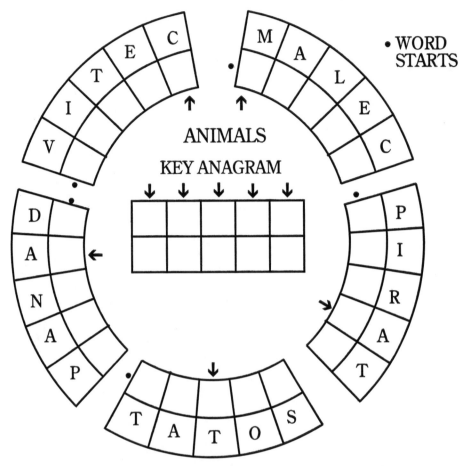

ANIMALS

WORD STARTS

ANIMALS

KEY ANAGRAM

The five 5-letter words have been jumbled. Solve the five anagrams of ANIMALS and then transfer the arrowed letters to the key anagram to find a sixth.

(Solution 48)

54 Something in Common

What do the answers to the following clues all have in common?

A small container   A European monetary currency
To enter abruptly   An inside covering
To strike smartly   To walk long and far
Easily damaged   Broker

(Solution 51)

55 Octagons

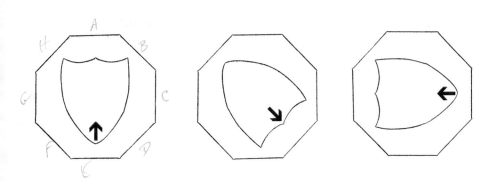

Which octagon comes next in the above sequence?

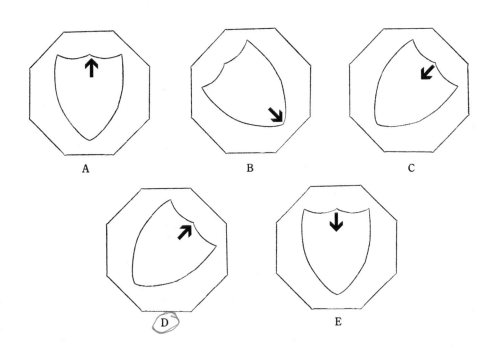

A   B   C

D   E

(Solution 55)

56 Cards

Permutation = Arrangements
How many 4-card permutations can you make in a pack of 52
playing cards?

(Solution 59)

57 Number Logic

Where, logically, would you place the number 1 in this grid?

					9	
	8					
			7			
6						5
3		4				
2						

(Solution 63)

58 Sequence

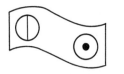 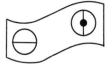 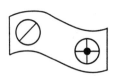

Which option below comes next in the above sequence?

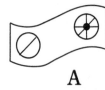 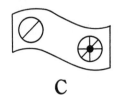 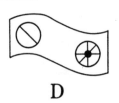

    A   B   C   D

(Solution 67)

59 *Word Power*

The answers are all 9-letter words and will be found in the grid one letter on each line in order.

C	G	P	R	M	D	F	M	O
B	A	E	U	E	A	U	L	A
S	C	S	J	A	B	N	R	L
E	L	G	T	K	U	I	A	S
C	A	S	U	I	Y	J	E	M
C	V	U	F	T	L	T	B	T
H	A	E	O	A	O	I	O	E
O	U	O	E	E	N	N	N	N
T	T	N	R	A	P	E	R	T

Clues:

1. To go stealthily
2. A soldier armed with hand fire-arms
3. Small ribbed melon
4. Seducer
5. Paving stone
6. Dried hemp
7. Reclining
8. Argument against
9. To gad about

(Solution 71)

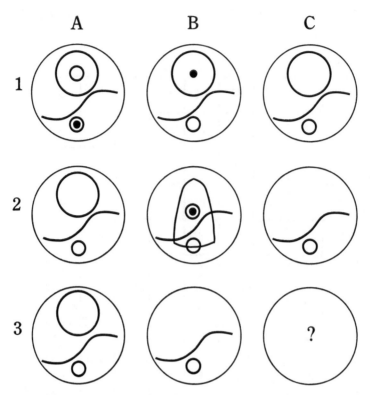

Logically which circle below fits into the above pattern?

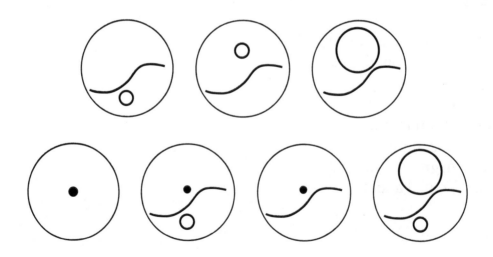

(Solution 75)

61 Pyramid

Spell out the 15-letter word by going into the pyramid one room at a time. Go into each room once only. You may go into the passage as many times as you wish.

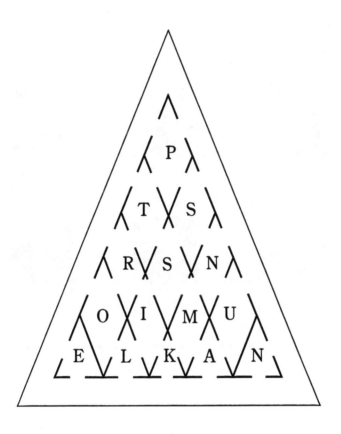

(Solution 78)

62 Sequence

ANDY, AMY, DES, DEAN, RUTH, RAY

What name below completes the above sequence?

TERRY, JANE, ALEC, BETH, TRUDY

(Solution 80)

63 Clueless Crossword

In each square there are four letters. Your task is to cross out three of each four, leaving one letter in each square, so that the crossword is made up in the usual way with good English interlocking words.

F P	J C	H A	M O	R B	O A	R S
Q T	U L	N U	E R	A T	E D	F L
P U	■	N O	■	U A	■	A L
L E	■	P E	■	E R	■	E O
L E	E A	P D	E A	R S	O N	L K
I A	N P	G A	N K	A T	I E	I M
E O	■	A E	■	E M	■	I A
T B	■	O N	■	S N	■	C E
K D	R U	D R	E S	P I	I E	D C
P E	I A	S E	A D	R T	C N	K G

(Solution 84)

64 Three Triangles

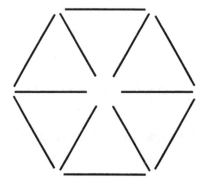

Move the position of only four matches to make three equilateral triangles.

(Solution 88)

65 Alternative Crossword

In the upper grid, the crossword letters have been replaced by numbers. Select the correct letter for each number from the three alternatives given, and enter the letter into the blank grid to make a crossword.

2	6	5	5	■	1	3	6	7
4	■	6	7	5	6	7	■	6
3	7	■	2	3	2	■	5	2
6	3	7	■	5	■	6	5	2
■	2	2	1	3	2	2	2	■
3	2	5	■	5	■	2	2	8
7	7	■	5	7	1	■	7	5
5	■	7	3	5	2	2	■	6
7	5	5	4	■	3	5	5	2

1	A B C
2	D E F
3	G H I
4	J K L
5	M N O
6	P Q R
7	S T U
8	V W X
9	Y Z

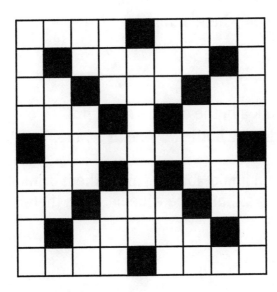

(Solution 93)

41

66 Circles

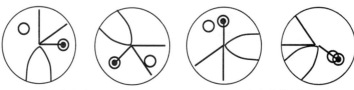

Which circle continues the sequence?

A   B   C   D   E

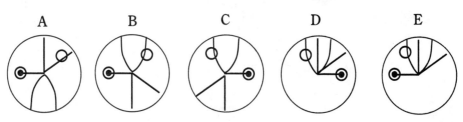

(Solution 96)

67 Square Roots

Does the number 6 2 4 9 7 3 2 3 have a square root composed of integers?

i.e.   √144 = 12, answer in integers

√141 = 11.874342 ......→ 00

(Note: Integers = whole numbers)

(Solution 100)

68 Wine

A man can drink a bottle of wine in 2½ hrs.
His wife can drink a bottle of wine in 1½ hrs.

How long would it take for the pair of them drinking at their respective rates to finish the wine between them?

(Solution 104)

69 Alternative Crossword

In the upper grid, the crossword letters have been replaced by numbers. Select the correct letter for each number from the three alternatives given, and enter the letter into the blank grid to make a crossword.

7	8	1	3	2
3	1	6	2	5
5	8	5	4	5
6	2	5	3	7
7	6	1	2	2

1	A	B	C
2	D	E	F
3	G	H	I
4	J	K	L
5	M	N	O
6	P	Q	R
7	S	T	U
8	V	W	X
9	Y	Z	–

(Solution 108)

43

70 Anagrammed Phrases

All the following are anagrams of well-known phrases. For example, SO NOTE HOLE = ON THE LOOSE.

1. SINGLE GLIDE LOSE PET

2. HUG TIGHT VETO POSE

3. BOTH ONES GET QUIET

4. HALF YELLOW ANT

5. YES LOOP A SAND FLAT

(Solution 112)

71 Work it Out

What number should replace the question mark?

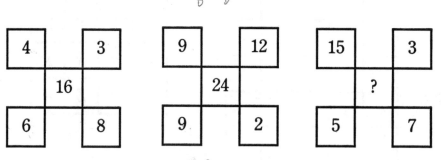

(Solution 117)

44

72 Cryptogram

This is a straight substitution cryptogram where each letter of the alphabet has been substituted for another.

CLUNK CK AZQC UX CLUNNKZ LUMYN,

CYKZ CK XKK UN CLUNNKZ CLUNK;

PSN CYKZ CK XKK UN CLUNNKZ CLUMYN,

CK AZQC 'NUX ZQN NYKZ CLUNNKZ LUMYN;

TQL CLUNK NQ YDFK UN CLUNNKZ LUMYN,

GSXN ZQN PK CLUNNKZ LUMYN ZQL CLUMYN;

ZQL BKN XYQSJV UN PK CLUNNKZ LUNK,

PSN CLUNK – TQL XQ 'NUX CLUNNKZ LUMYN.

(Solution 122)

73 Sequence

Which of the following comes next in the above sequence?

A   B   C   D

(Solution 126)

74 Sequence

RAYON, EPAULET, WORTH, ?

What word below continues the above sequence?
ITINERARY, ROMANCED, CARDIGAN, REEF, CHANCE

(Solution 130)

75 Threes

Can you group these into sets of three?

ROOKS   WHALES   PIGS
MACHINE GUNS   ACTORS   HIPPOPOTAMUSES
SCOUTS   OXEN   WASPS
HYENAS   SEALS   SWINE
PEAS   BABOONS   MICE
WOLVES   PENGUINS   CIGARETTES

(Solution 136)

76 Common

What do these words have in common?

1. BIBBER
2. PRACTICAL
3. BADLY
4. BARCELONA
5. RAGGED
6. EDITOR
7. TWENTY
8. ACROSS

(Solution 139)

77 Scales

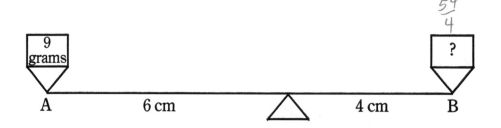

What value weight should be placed on the scales at B to balance the scales?

(Solution 143)

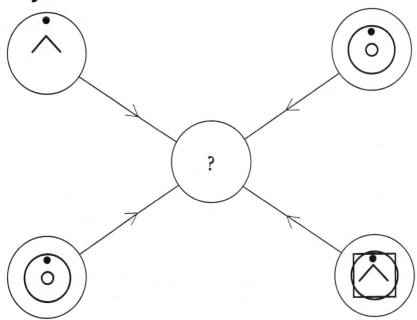

Each line and symbol which appears in the four outer circles is transferred to the center circle according to these rules:

If a line or symbol occurs in the outer circle:

once   it is transferred
twice   it is possibly transferred
three times   it is transferred
four times   it is not transferred

Which of the circles A, B, C, D, or E, shown below, should appear at the center of the diagram?

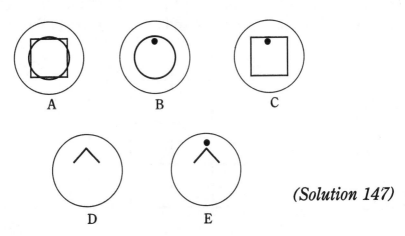

A   B   C

D   E

(Solution 147)

47

79 Eponyms

An eponym is a word which is derived from the name of a person because of their invention, action, or product. For example, the word "ampère" is derived from the French physicist André Marie Ampère and the word "mausoleum" after the tomb of a 4th-century B.C. king, Mausolus.

Can you identify the eponyms from the following definitions?

1. A close-fitting garment, from a 19th-century trapeze artist.
2. Very harsh, after a 7th-century B.C. Greek lawmaker.
3. Nonconformist, after a 19th-century Texas rancher.
4. A type of sweater, after a 19th-century British general.
5. A spiritual relationship, after a Greek philosopher.
6. Sumptuous banquets, after a 1st-century B.C. Roman general.
7. A strict disciplinarian, after a 17th-century French drill master.
8. Dull-witted, after attempts to ridicule followers of an 11–12th-century Scottish theologian.
9. Spellbind or enchant, after an 18–19th-century German physician.
10. Crafty or deceitful, after a 15–16th-century Florentine statesman.

(Solution 152)

80 Magic "34"

Arrange the remaining digits from 1 to 16 to form a magic square where each horizontal, vertical, and corner-to-corner line totals 34.

			16
	12		
4			
		8	

(Solution 2)

81 Square Numbers

Each horizontal and vertical line contains the digits of a 4-figure square number. All digits are in the correct order but not necessarily adjacent. All digits are used only once.

4	4	9	4	8	1	9	2
1	1	6	2	8	1	3	2
2	7	8	9	5	4	1	6
3	9	6	3	0	4	1	0
6	2	0	0	9	4	4	1
5	6	3	0	2	2	3	5
5	4	1	4	7	7	6	6
6	3	1	3	9	4	6	9

(Solution 6)

82 Middle Letters

Find the complete words that contain these middle letters.

SSB*
ISERL
ZZYW*
NGIP
NKEYD
USTJ*
RFETC
TEDDF
ISYC*
PPLEG*

* These words are hyphenated

(Solution 10)

83 Sequence

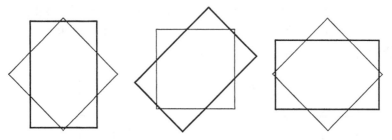

Which of the options below continues the above sequence?

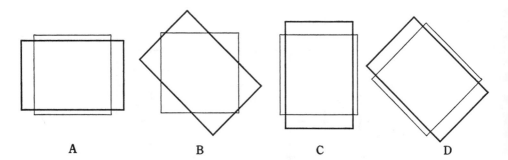

A   B   C   D

(Solution 14)

84 Baby

How heavy was the baby at birth? asked the mother.
The nurse replied 12.96 lbs, divided by 1/4 of his own weight.

How much did the baby weigh?

$$\frac{12.96}{w/4} = w \qquad \boxed{w = 7.2}$$

$$w^2 = 51.84$$

(Solution 18)

85 Names

What have the following names got in common?

STAN, TINA, MARK, DAN

(Solution 22)

86 Do-it-Yourself Crossword

Place the pieces in the grid in order to complete the crossword.

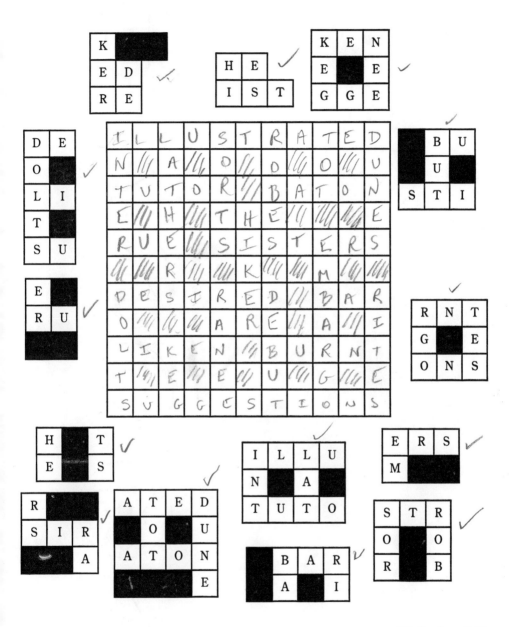

(Solution 26)

87 Comparison

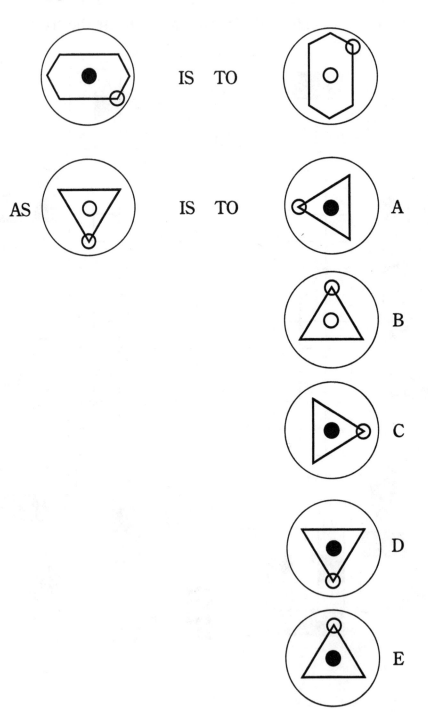

IS TO

AS

IS TO

A

B

C

D

E

(Solution 30)

88 The Puzzling Puzzle

Start at the middle square and work from square to square horizontally, vertically, or diagonally to spell out six puzzling words. Every square must be visited only once and every square is used. Finish at the top right-hand square.

U	N	O	S	M	E	T	→
N	C	T	E	Y	R	N	
R	D	Y	R	M	I	E	
N	U	M	*	W	D	L	
I	E	D	O	E	B	M	
M	G	A	R	X	O	E	
A	P	A	P	R	L	B	

Handwritten annotations on the grid:
- Superscripts/numbers: U², N², O², N², C², R², D², N₃, E₃ (various)
- Handwritten solution list to the right:
  1 MYSTERY
  2 CONUNDRUM
  3 ENIGMA
  4 PARADOX
  5 PROBLEM
  6 ... RMENT

(Solution 34)

89 Bath

You are trying to fill a bath with both taps full on, but have accidentally left out the plug. Normally the hot water tap takes eight minutes to fill the bath and the cold water tap takes ten minutes. However, the water empties out through the plug hole in five minutes. How long will it take for the bath to fill?

(Solution 38)

Handwritten working:

$x = time$

$$\frac{x}{8} + \frac{x}{10} - \frac{x}{5} = 1$$

$$x \cdot \frac{5 + 4 - 8}{40} = 1$$

$$\boxed{x = 40}$$

90 Circles

What should be the contents of the circle with the question mark?

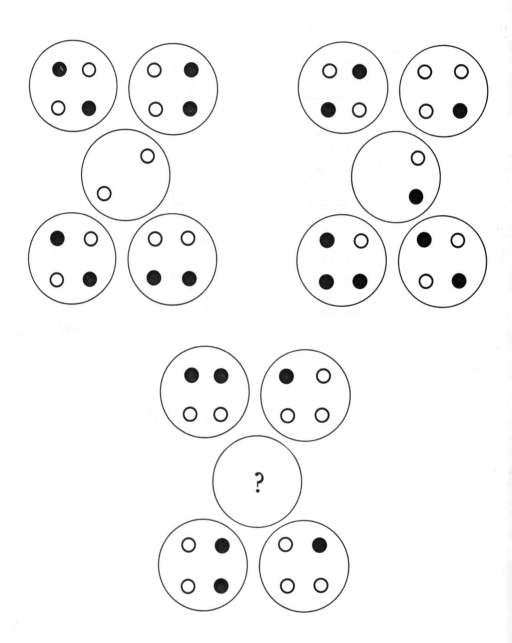

(Solution 43)

91 Fish

Change one letter of each answer to obtain the name of a fish.

		ANSWER	FISH
1.	CORRECT	_ _ _ _ _ _	* _ _ _ _ _
2.	KINE	_ _ _ _ _ _	_ * _ _ _ _
3.	ARTILLERYMAN	_ _ _ _ _ _	_ _ _ _ _ *
4.	SMALL CHILD	_ _ _ _ _ _	* _ _ _ _ _
5.	STUPID PERSON	_ _ _ _ _ _ _	* _ _ _ _ _ _
6.	RESENTMENT	_ _ _ _ _ _	* _ _ _ _ _
7.	ENGINEER	_ _ _ _ _ _	* _ _ _ _ _
8.	VISION	SIGHT	* _ _ _ _
9.	AMMUNITION	_ _ _ _ _ _	* _ _ _ _

(Solution 47)

92 Odd One Out

Which is the odd one?

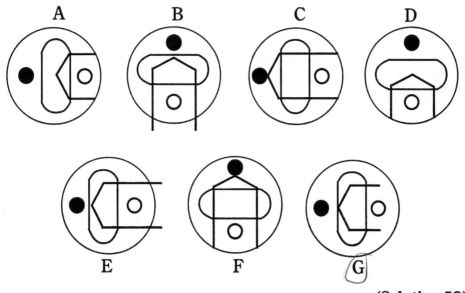

(Solution 52)

93 Nursery Rhyme Crossword

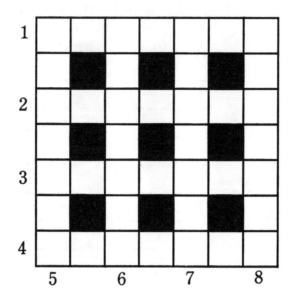

In the narrative are eight clues. Find them, solve them, and then place the answers in the grid.

4. The longed for number, four and twenty blackbirds,
3. were dealt with, by being baked in a pie
2. they tried to reinstate it,
8. the birds gave out a song
5. that deserved being called a dainty dish, to place before the king who was called
1. His Greatness
6. by the buffoons
7. who arrived on a wheeled footboard.

(Solution 57)

56

94 Network

Find the starting point and travel along the connecting lines in a continuous path to adjacent circles to spell out a 14-letter word. Every circle must be visited only once.

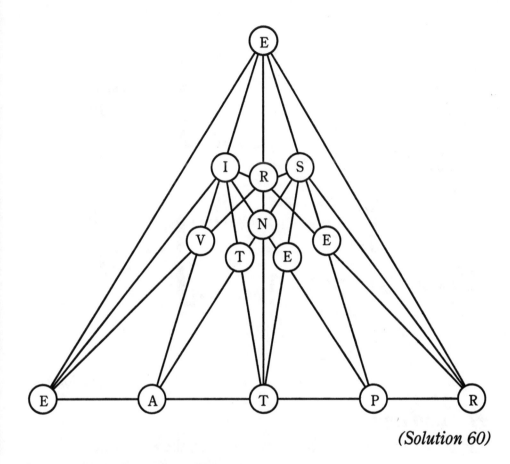

(Solution 60)

95 Find Another Word

BELOW, ORE, ROWER

Which word below goes with the three words above?
BOAT, LONG, SHORE, CARRY, WIND

(Solution 64)

96 Connections

Each pair of words, by meaning or association, leads to another word. Find the missing words 18–30. The number of letters in the missing words are indicated by the dots.

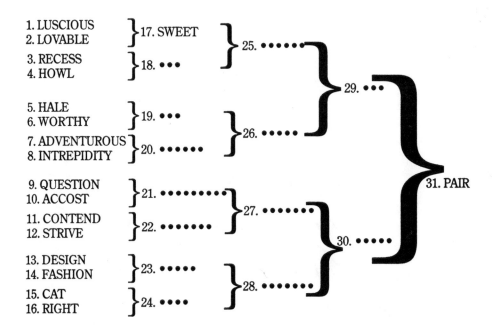

1. LUSCIOUS
2. LOVABLE
} 17. SWEET
3. RECESS
4. HOWL
} 18. •••
} 25. ••••••
5. HALE
6. WORTHY
} 19. •••
7. ADVENTUROUS
8. INTREPIDITY
} 20. ••••••
} 26. ••••••
29. •••
9. QUESTION
10. ACCOST
} 21. •••••••••
11. CONTEND
12. STRIVE
} 22. •••••••
} 27. ••••••••
13. DESIGN
14. FASHION
} 23. •••••
15. CAT
16. RIGHT
} 24. ••••
} 28. •••••••
30. ••••••
31. PAIR

(Solution 69)

97 Ending

Find a 3-letter word which when placed on the end of these words make new words.

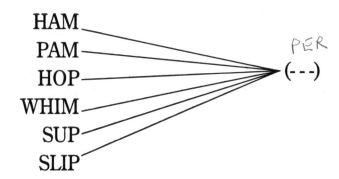

HAM
PAM
HOP
WHIM
SUP
SLIP

PER
(- - -)

(Solution 72)

58

Which option below continues the above sequence?

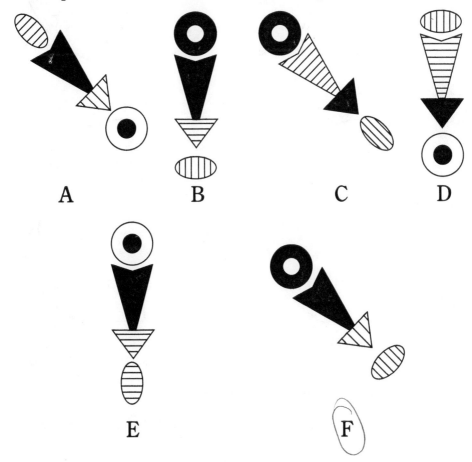

A   B   C   D

E   F

(Solution 76)

99 Safe

In order to open the safe, you have to rotate the wheels to find a 4-letter word.

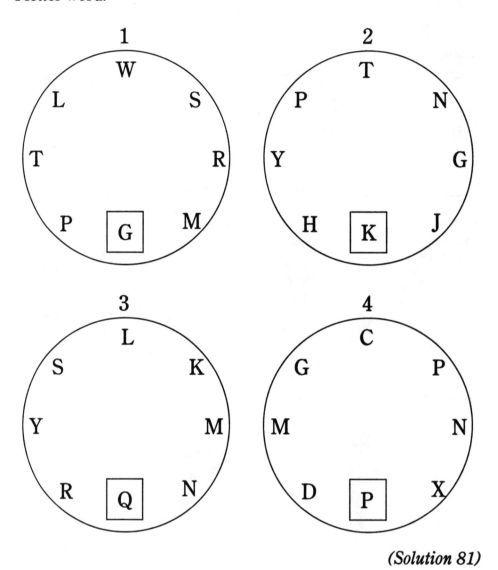

(Solution 81)

100 Complete the Calculation

Insert the same number twice (not the number 1) to make this calculation correct.

$$6 \div 6 = 6$$

(Solution 85)

101 Grid

Each of the nine squares 1A to 3C should incorporate all the lines and symbols which are shown in the outer squares marked A, B, or C and 1, 2, or 3. Thus 2B should incorporate all the lines and symbols in 2 and B.

2 A

One of the squares, 1A to 3C, is incorrect. Which one is it?

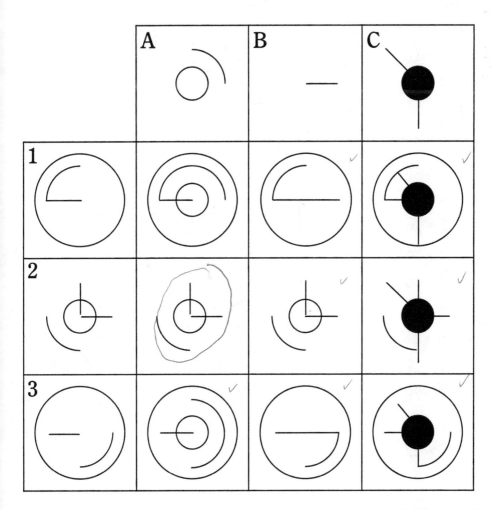

(Solution 89)

61

102 Connections

Insert the numbers 0–10 in the circles opposite, so that for any particular circle the sum of the numbers in the circles connected directly to it equals the value corresponding to the number in that circle, as given in the list.

Example:

1 = 14 (4 + 7 + 3)

4 = 8 (7 + 1)

7 = 5 (4 + 1)

3 = 1

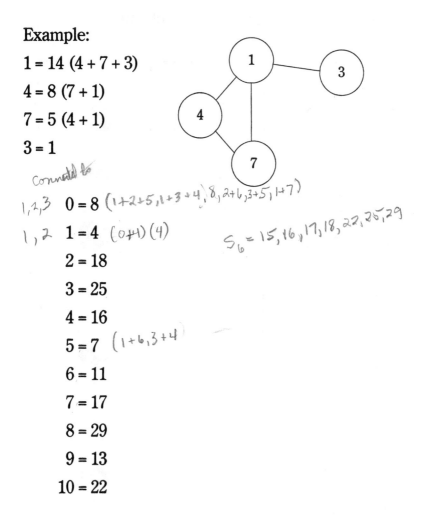

Connected to

1,2,3 0 = 8 (1+2+5, 1+3+4, 8, 2+6, 3+5, 1+7)

1,2 1 = 4 (0+1) (4) S_6 = 15, 16, 17, 18, 22, 26, 29

2 = 18

3 = 25

4 = 16

5 = 7 (1+6, 3+4)

6 = 11

7 = 17

8 = 29

9 = 13

10 = 22

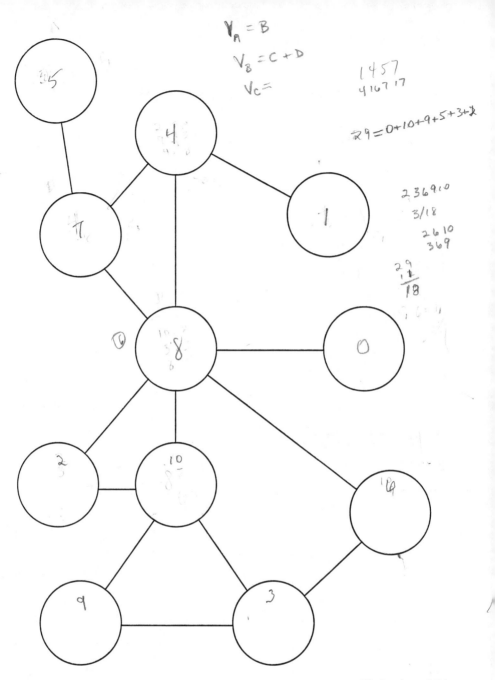

(Solution 98)

103 No Neighbors

Unscramble the letters to find an 18-letter word. There are no two adjoining letters in the same shape.

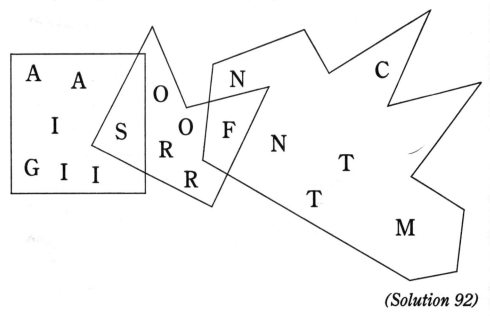

(Solution 92)

104 Missing Links

From the information provided fill in the missing numbers. The link between the numbers in each line is the same.

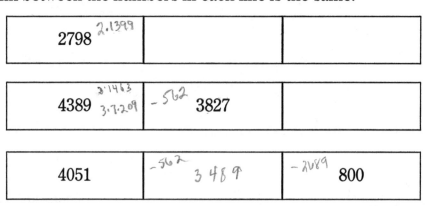

(Solution 101)

105 Occupations

These thirty-six 3-letter bits can be grouped to form
twelve 9-letter words which are all occupations.

³PRO	''KER	⁹BAL	¹²NOT
¹ºATH	⁴PUP	¹KEE	¹ºOST
¹²HYP	¹ºEOP	⁷MAJ	⁹HER
⁴EER	¹ZOO	⁹IST	⁷ORD
¹²IST	⁶PLO	⁴PET	⁸GON
²GEO	²LOG	¹PER	⁶UGH
⁷OMO	³FES	⁵POO	⁵NER
¹¹ROP	¹¹EMA	³SOR	¹²IST
⁶MAN	⁵HAR	⁸IER	⁸DOL

1 ZOOKEEPER
2 GEOLOGIST
3 PROFESSOR
4 PUPPETEER
5 HARPOONER
6 PLOUGHMAN
7 MAJORDOMO
8 GONDOLIER
9 HERBALIST
10 OSTEOPATH
11 ROPEMAKER
12 HYPNOTIST

geologist
zoologist

(Solution 106)

106 Sea Level

If you were standing on top of a 50-foot-high cliff, how far would
you be able to see out to sea?

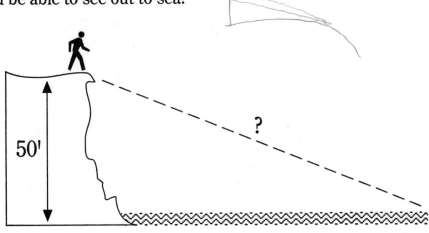

(Solution 109)

65

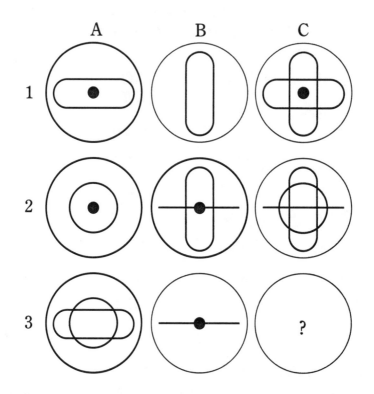

Logically which circle below fits into the above pattern?

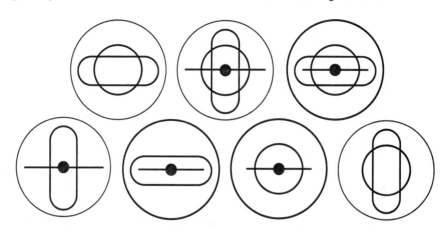

(Solution 113)

108 Quotation

Rearrange the words to form a quotation. The boxed letters spell out the name of the quotation's author.

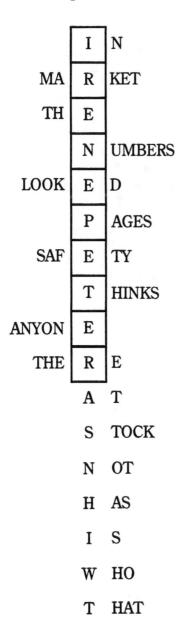

	I	N
MA	R	KET
TH	E	
	N	UMBERS
LOOK	E	D
	P	AGES
SAF	E	TY
	T	HINKS
ANYON	E	
THE	R	E
	A	T
	S	TOCK
	N	OT
	H	AS
	I	S
	W	HO
	T	HAT

(Solution 120)

109 Dominoes

Draw in the lines of the twenty-eight dominoes, which are from 0–0 to 6–6.

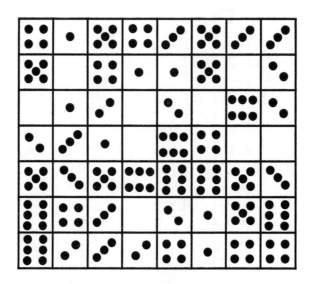

(Solution 123)

110 Letter Sequence

What letter comes next in this sequence?

TENTDTTSFM?

(Solution 127)

111 Odd One Out

Which of these words is the odd one out?

TEN ONE STONE OPEN
TENT TOE OFTEN SON

(Solution 131)

112 Missing Number

What number should replace the question mark?

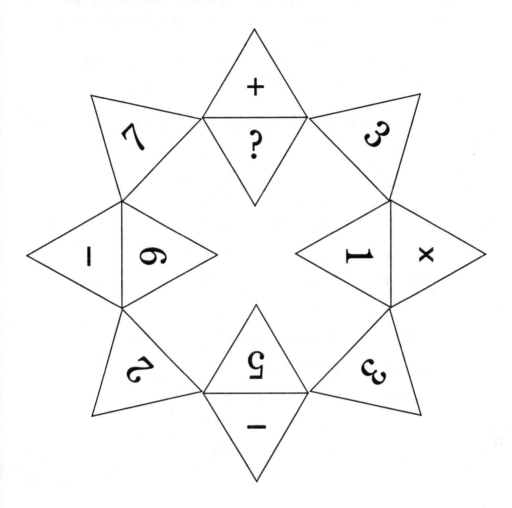

(Solution 134)

113 Middle Words

In each of the following insert a word in the bracket which when tacked onto the end of the first word forms a new word, and when placed in front of the second word forms another word.

For example: ARC (•••) RING. Answer: HER – to form the words ARCHER and HERRING.

The number of dots indicates the number of letters in the word to be inserted.

1.	GRUB	(••)	WAY
2.	MAR	(••••)	PIN
3.	OF	(••••)	PLATE
4.	ORANGE	(••••)	PILE
5.	SO	(••)	SON
6.	STAR	(••••)	LET
7.	DIGIT	(•••)	LIER
8.	WAR	(•••••)	UP
9.	WRIT	(••)	ART
10.	MOB	(•••)	RICE

(Solution 140)

70

114 Track Word

Work around the track to find a 15-letter word. You have to provide the missing letters and find the starting point. The word might appear reading clockwise or counterclockwise, and the overlapping letter appears twice.

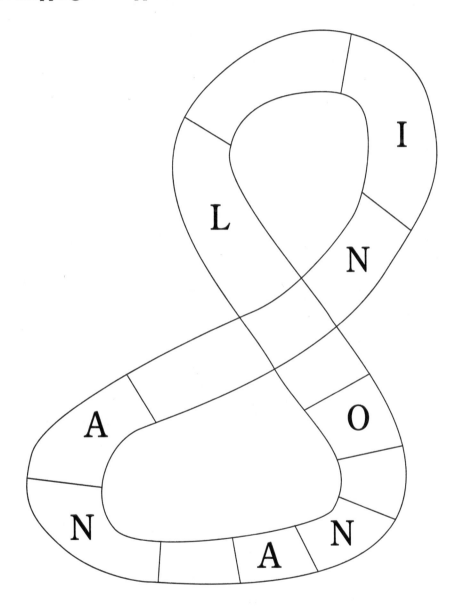

(Solution 144)

115 *Quotation*

Rearrange the words to read out a quotation by Will Rogers.

CAN'T	IT	WAS	MINUTE	SURE
DRAWN	UNDERSTAND	THE	BE	READ
SOMETHING	BY	YOU	UP	YOU
YOU	ALMOST	A	CAN	LAWYER

(Solution 148)

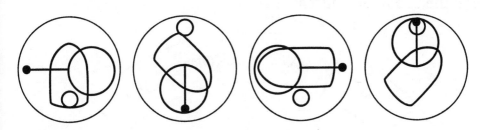

Which option below continues the above sequence?

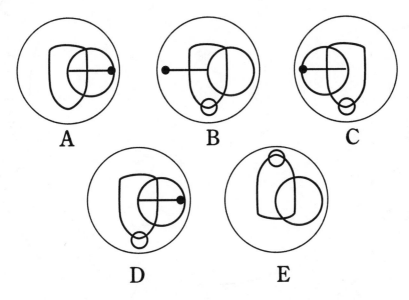

A   B   C

D   E

(Solution 153)

117 Quotation by Mark Twain

Find the quotation. Start at "I".

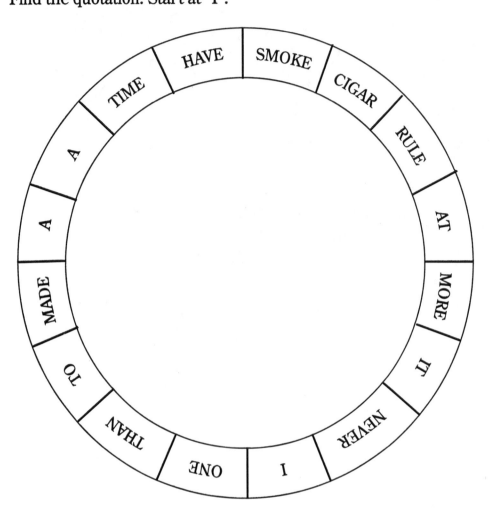

(Solution 156)

118 Spots

When spots are placed on the circumference and then joined, regions will be formed.

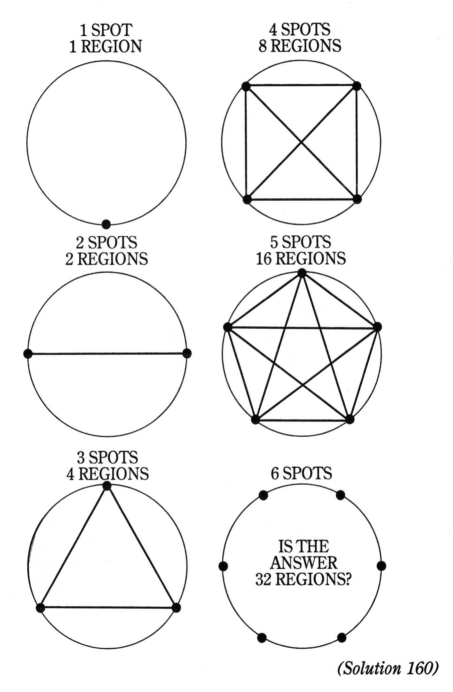

1 SPOT
1 REGION

4 SPOTS
8 REGIONS

2 SPOTS
2 REGIONS

5 SPOTS
16 REGIONS

3 SPOTS
4 REGIONS

6 SPOTS

IS THE
ANSWER
32 REGIONS?

(Solution 160)

119   The Hexagonal Pyramid

Work out the contents of the top hexagon.

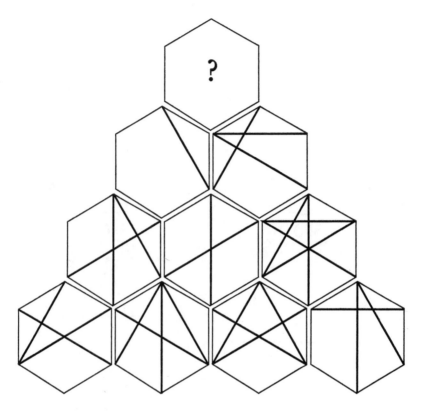

(Solution 158)

120   Synchronized Synonyms

Each grid contains the letters of eight 8-letter words. All letters are in the correct order and each letter is used only once. Each word in Grid One has a synonym in Grid Two and the letters of each of the eight pairs of synonyms are in exactly the same position in each grid. Clues to each pair of synonyms are given in no particular order.

Example: The answers to the clue VAST are the words TOWERING in Grid One and GIGANTIC in Grid Two.

Find the remaining seven pairs of synonyms.

D	D	S	L	D	C	I	I
A	A	(T)	W	E	S	S	X
T	I	I	I	L	(O)	T	O
L	E	A	T	N	R	R	N
D	E	D	(W)	A	L	(E)	U
D	L	O	C	U	L	T	T
A	(R)	E	O	(I)	E	(N)	E
R	W	O	D	S	(G)	R	R

Grid One

P	P	D	W	G	S	S	R
C	I	(G)	E	O	O	E	L
D	C	O	E	H	(I)	N	L
I	E	C	I	D	V	S	E
U	E	I	(G)	T	L	(A)	E
S	V	H	R	E	U	N	A
L	(N)	E	D	(T)	R	(I)	S
R	E	O	Y	D	(C)	E	R

Grid Two

Clues: VAST, SLICK, CHIEF, LONE, TWISTER, DIARY, FORBID, BREADTH

(Solution 159)

77

121 Brain Strain

Insert the missing numbers so that the calculations are correct, both across and down. All numbers to be inserted are less than 10 (there is no zero).

	+		−		=	9
+	■	+	■	+	■	×
	+		−	6	=	
−	■	÷	■	−	■	÷
	+	4	−		=	
=	■	=	■	=	■	=
6	÷		+		=	

(Solution 3)

122 Circle

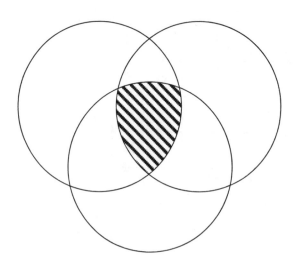

Approximately how much of one circle is shaded?

(Solution 7)

78

123 "E" Frame

All vowels are "E" and are not shown. All consonants are shown and all are used once only. "42" means four consonants and two vowels.

DOWN

	1	2	3	4	5	6	7	8	
1	R	L	S	P	T	L	D	T	42
2	Y	P	L	S	D	T	L	P	52
3	B	B	B	P	D	H	W	L	42
4	K	J	R	N	S	N	N	T	42
5	L	D	N	P	L	S	N	S	52
6	N	R	L	K	R	T	N	B	42
7	W	R	C	R	F	B	D	M	32
8	N	T	H	T	M	R	F	M	32
	42	42	42	42	42	42	42	42	

(ACROSS — left label)

Clues:

Across

1. Arid land
2. Walked carefully
3. Duck-like feet
4. Small house
5. Never ceasing
6. Dog's house
7. Put off
8. Go in

Down

1. Happening every seven days
2. Threefold
3. Man addicted to lewdness
4. Condiment
5. Nothing more
6. A worshipping place
7. Yellow flowering plant
8. Symbolic representation

(Solution 12)

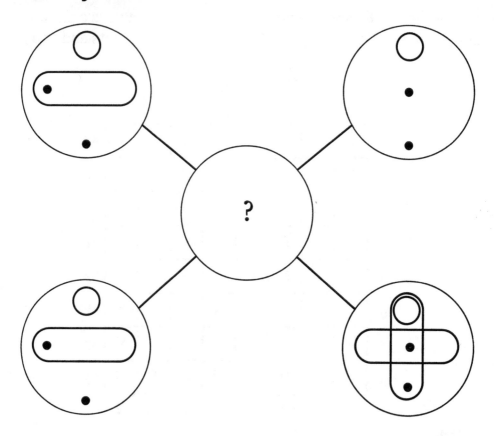

Each line and symbol which appears in the four outer circles is transferred to the center circle according to these rules:

If a line or symbol occurs in the outer circle:

once | it is transferred
twice | it is possibly transferred
three times | it is tranferred
four times | it is not transferred

Which of the circles A, B, C, D, or E, shown opposite, should appear at the center of the diagram?

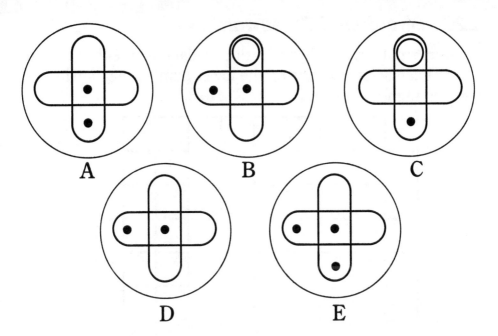

A B C

D E

(Solution 15)

125 *Add a Letter*

Find a letter in place of "?" so that when it is added to each of the
5-letter sets and rearranged, 6-letter words will be formed.

The 6-letter words are names of plants and trees.

	C	H	E	W	S
	C	H	U	M	S
?	G	O	N	E	R
	C	H	O	R	E
	S	E	E	M	S

(Solution 19)

126 Directional Crossword

Answers run horizontally, vertically, or diagonally, either to right or left. Each solution starts on the lower number and finishes on the next higher number, i.e., 1 to 2, 2 to 3, etc.

1. Mislead
2. Anti-perspirant
3. Stormy
4. Wave passing around the earth
5. Learned
6. Talk over
7. Ship
8. Mechanical man
9. Controllable
10. Descriptive term
11. Leaves for smoking
12. Exposed
13. Girl's name
14. Gilbert and Sullivan's "____men" guardians
15. Hotchpotch
16. Musical instrument
17. Make a mistake

(Solution 24)

127 Quartering a Square

Divide the square into four quarters. Each quarter should be the same size and shape and contain the same four symbols.

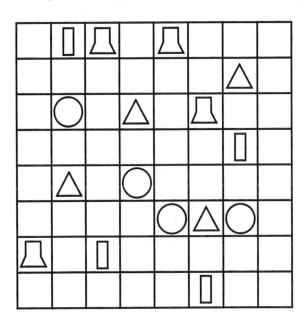

(Solution 28)

128 Concentration

A B C D E F G H

What letter is two to the right of the letter immediately to the right of the letter four to the left of the letter two to the right of the letter four to the right of the letter immediately to the left of the letter which comes midway between the letter two to the left of the letter "C" and the letter three to the left of the letter "F"?

(Solution 31)

129 Polling Day

At a recent election a total of 23,968 votes were cast for the four candidates, the winner exceeding his opponents by 1026, 2822, and 6428 votes respectively.

How many votes were received by each candidate?

(Solution 35)

130 Alternatives

Select the correct meaning from the three alternatives.

1. Canicular
   (a) Oval-shaped
   (b) Bearing flowers
   (c) Pertaining to the Dog-Star

2. Dipsas
   (a) A snake
   (b) A verse of 5 lines
   (c) A drunkard

3. Escadrille
   (a) A flotilla
   (b) A shoe
   (c) A platoon

4. Fon
   (a) Phonetic
   (b) A fool
   (c) Telephone

5. Griffon
   (a) A terrier
   (b) A light snack
   (c) A waterspout

6. Ikebana
   (a) Flower arranging
   (b) Exercise routine
   (c) A waterfall

7. Lempira
   (a) Monetary unit of Honduras
   (b) Circular motion
   (c) A drug

8. Mazzard
   (a) Skull
   (b) Drizzle
   (c) Food

(Solution 39)

131 Ten-Digit Number

Write down a 10-digit number such that:
The 1st digit indicates the total number of 1's
The 2nd digit indicates the total number of 2's
The 3rd digit indicates the total number of 3's, etc., to the 10th
digit, which indicates the total number of zeroes.

(Solution 42)

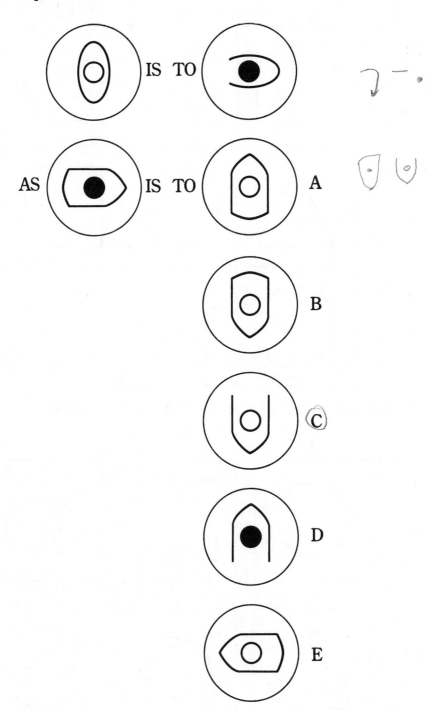

IS TO

AS ... IS TO ... A

B

C

D

E

(Solution 45)

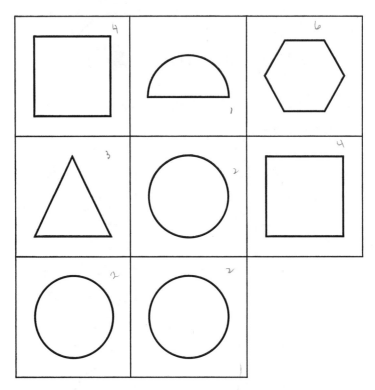

Choose the missing square from the options below.

A   B   C

D   E   F

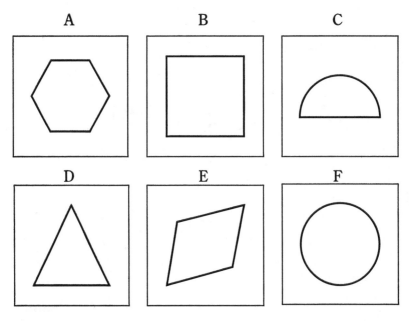

(Solution 49)

134 Found in the USA

All the following are anagrams of things which can be found in the USA.

1.   MINUTE BATH STEEP GRID LIE
2.   AND TRY NO CHANGE
3.   SKATE ALERT GAL
4.   NUN I'M STRAY COOK
5.   HAIL GAME NICK
6.   I HE SHE WE TO HUT

(Solution 53)

135 Odd One Out

Which is the odd one?

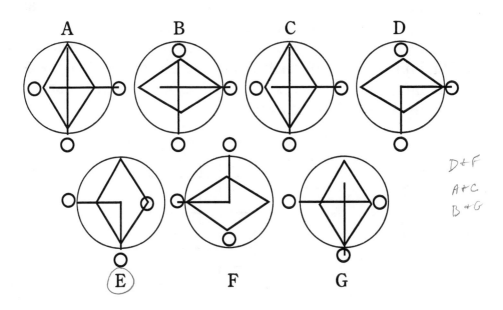

(Solution 56)

87

136 Anagram Theme

Arrange the fourteen words in pairs so that each pair is an anagram of another word or name. The seven words produced will have a linking theme. For example, if the words TRY and CREASE were in the list, they could be paired to form an anagram of SECRETARY and the theme could be PROFESSIONS.

AGE	AURA	DIN	END	
FLAN	GAIN	GRAIN	HAY	SEW
IRE	NEAT	RAIL	RUNG	SIT

(Solution 62)

137 Nines

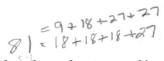

A number is divisible by 9 exactly when the sum of its digits are also divisible by 9 exactly. For example, the number 7866 is divisible by 9 because 7 + 8 + 6 + 6 = 27, which is also divisible by 9. With this in mind, place the digits into the grid so that the 4-figure numbers in all horizontal, vertical, and corner-to-corner lines are exactly divisible by 9.

1, 1,
2,
3, 3, 3,
5, 5,
6, 6, 6,
7,
8, 8, 8,
9.

(Solution 65)

138 Missing Letters

Fill in the missing letters to make ten occupations.

1. • N • T • M • S •
2. • T • N • M • N
3. • O • T • W • I •
4. • I • E • T • R
5. • A • A • N • R
6. • I • T • C • A •
7. • S • E • E • T •
8. • I • L • N • S •
9. • E • C • N • R •
10. • A • F • T • E •

(Solution 68)

139 Sequence

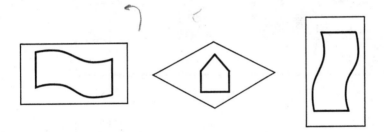

Which option below continues the above sequence?

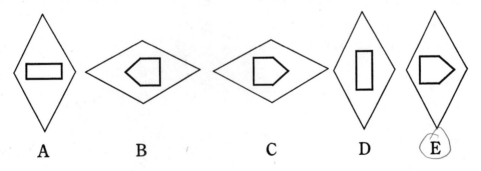

A   B   C   D   E

(Solution 73)

140 Niners

Solve the eight clues.

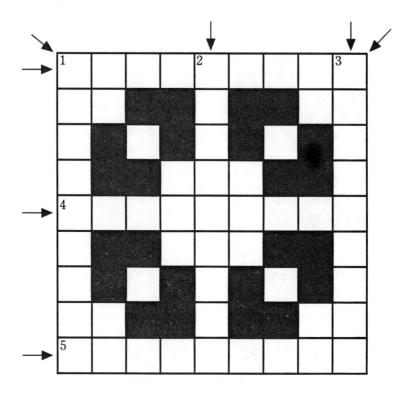

Clues:

Across
1. Declarer
4. Ramp or bridge
5. For boiling water

Down
1. Revolutionist
2. Frankness
3. Of a definition

Diagonal
1. Chargeable
2. Coming into renewed life

(Solution 77)

141 Safe

The safe can only be opened by pressing the buttons in the correct order, following the directions on each button. The last button is marked (0). You have to find the 1st button.

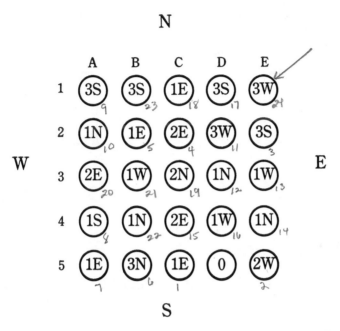

(Solution 82)

142 Song

This verse of an old song has had all of its vowels removed and is written in groups of five. See if you can reconstitute it and make it into its words.

all around the mulberry bush ...

LLRND	THMLB	RRYBS
HTHM	NKYCH	SDTHW
SLTHM	NKYTH	GHTTW
SSCHF	NPPGS	THWSL

(Solution 86)

143 Pyramid Word

Solve the five clues, place the five words in the pyramid, then rearrange all fifteen letters to find a 15-letter word.

- abbreviation for pound sterling (1)
- the ratio of the circumference of a circle to its diameter (2)
- weapon (3)
- family of ruminant animals (4)
- convey in a vehicle (5)

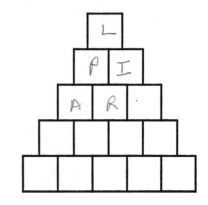

(Solution 90)

144 Middle Word

Place a word in the brackets which means the same as the words or phrases outside the brackets.

1. A Chinese idol (- - - -) Fate
2. Triangular sail (- - -) To balk
3. Branched candleholder (- - - - -- - - -) Rotating firework
4. Wolverine (- - - - - --) One who eats to excess
5. Stuffing (- - - - -) Buffoonery
6. Young deer (- - - -) To flatter
7. Polecat (- - - ---) Search out
8. Polecat (- - - - - -) Vetch
9. Darling (- - - - - -) Lathe-head
10. Broken piece (- - - - -) Beetle's wing case

(Solution 94)

145 Cross-Alphabet

Insert the letters of the alphabet only once each into the grid to form a crossword. Clues are given, but in no particular order.

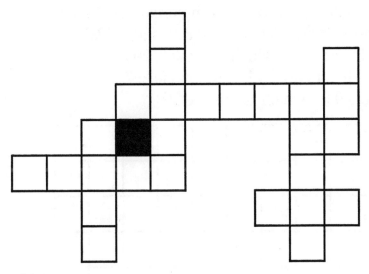

Clues:
- correctly
- side post of a door
- vessel in which consecrated host is preserved
- beast of burden
- adored
- speedy
- swagger
- Turkish cap

(Solution 97)

146 Number Sequence

What number comes next in this sequence?

1, 8, 70, 627, 5639, ?

(Solution 102)

147 Multiple Magic

Fill in the remaining numbers from 1 to 81 to form a multiple magic square to produce:

1. A 3 × 3 inner core where each horizontal, vertical, and corner-to-corner line totals 123 (a magic 123)
2. A 5 × 5 inner core which is a magic 205
3. A 7 × 7 inner core which is a magic 287
4. A whole 9 × 9 which is a magic 369

		63						
81								1
		36		45				
				41				
	18			37				
	72							
						27	56	
					9			

(Solution 105)

148 Three Squares

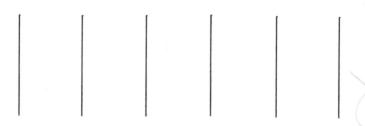

Using only six matchsticks create three squares of equal size. This one calls for a bit of lateral thinking.

(Solution 110)

149 Plan in Works

Change one letter from each word to make, in each case, a well-known phrase, for example:
   PET RICE QUACK = GET RICH QUICK

1.   GO PUT IN FIRE
2.   PIN HARDS TOWN
3.   BOOK HERS
4.   PULL AT PITCH LATER
5.   FASTS ON LINE
6.   TALL IF FIRM
7.   GO SICK SHE MUST
8.   SET START
9.   RUM TUM
10.   FOE IN MY
11.   NOW GO SAD
12.   SO CRY BUT

(Solution 115)

150 Odd One Out

Which is the odd one?

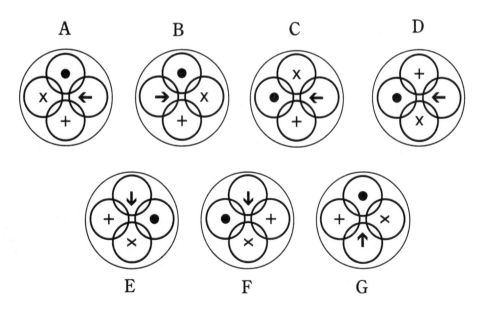

(Solution 155)

151 Trios

Complete the words to find, in each set, three words which are synonyms. For example:

IN • • N •   = INVENT
• • I • IN • • •   = ORIGINATE
• • • I • N   = DESIGN

1. A • • • • T • • • T   4. G • A • • • • •
    • A • • AT • • •   • • A • • • • G
    A • T • • AT • • •   • • • GA • •

2. • • SS • • • O •   5. • • • • IT • • •
    • O • • • • S • O •   I • IT • TI • •
    • • SO • • • • O •   • • • • T • • • • • IT

3. • • V • • E   6. • W • • E •
    • EVE • E •   • • • E • • W • • E
    VE • E • • • • E   WE • • E

                                            (Solution 154)

152 Number

Which number should go in D?

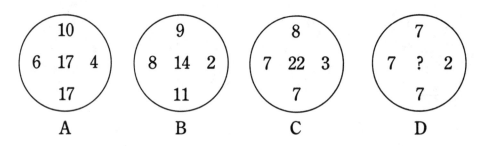

A   B   C   D

(Solution 150)

96

153 Brackets

Place a word in the brackets that when added on to the end of the first word forms a new word or phrase, and when placed in front of the second word also forms a new word or phrase.

1. RAIN   (- - - - -)   READER
2. LAMP   (- - - - -)   HOUSE
3. HORSE   (- - - -)   GROUND
4. HORSE   (- - - -)   HAND
5. FLINT   (- - - -)   SMITH
6. CROSS   (- - - -)   LAND
7. BRUSH   (- - - -)   WOOD
8. DRAGON   (- - -)   FISHING
9. DREAM   (- - - -)   LOCKED
10. BALL   (- - - - -)   LESS

(Solution 149)

154 Magic Square

The answers to the five clues are all 5-letter words, which when placed correctly in the grid form a magic word square where the same five words can be read both horizontally and vertically.

Clues (in no particular order):
- In Roman times the ninth
  day before the Ides
- An appointed meeting
- Anguish
- Stiffness
- To bestow

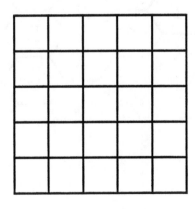

(Solution 145)

155 1 − 2 − 3

Fill in the last line to a regular rule.

1
11
21
1211
111221
312211
13112221

‒‒‒‒‒‒‒‒‒‒?

(Solution 141)

156 Honeycomb

Reading in any direction, find sixteen animals. Letters may be used more than once in the same word.

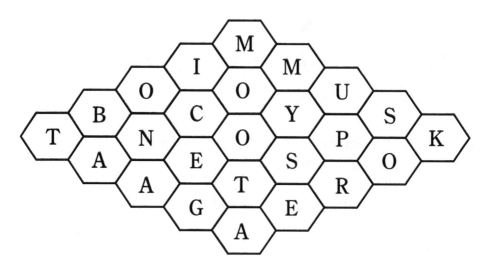

(Solution 137)

157 Missing Number

What is the missing number?

7	4	6	11
8	8	1	15
5	6	8	?

(Solution 132)

158 Pyramid Quotation

"Etiquette is the noise you don't make while having soup."

Using all 45 letters of the above quotation only once, complete the pyramid with
1 × 1-letter,
1 × 2-letters,
1 × 3-letter words, etc.

Clues are given, but in no particular order.

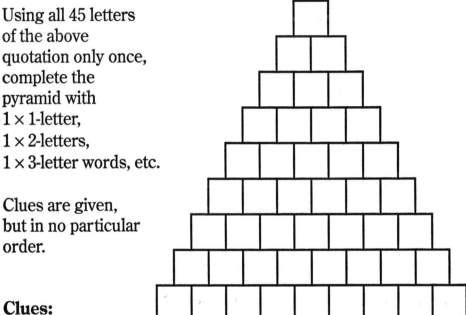

Clues:
- Loud cry
- Crib
- Ornamental discs on dresses
- Large spotted dog
- An exclamation of surprise
- Steal
- Formal written application to persons in authority
- Very big
- The first person plural pronoun

(Solution 128)

159 Circles

Which of these fit into the blank circle to carry on a logical sequence?

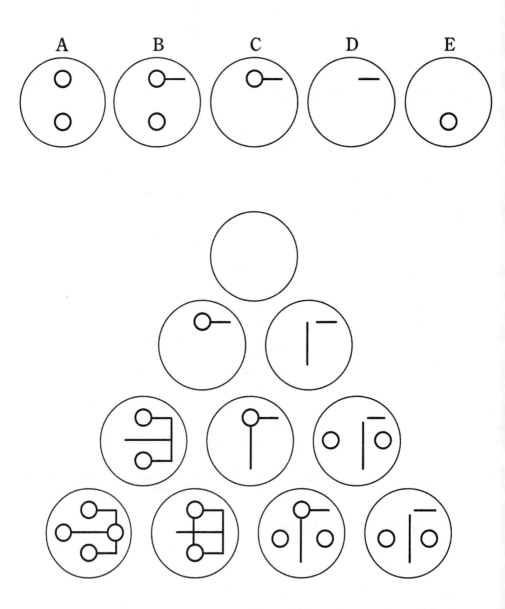

(Solution 125)

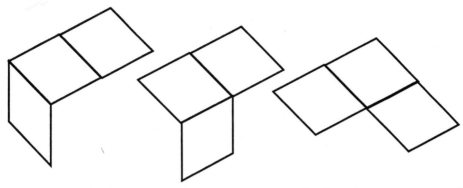

Which of the following options comes next in the above sequence?

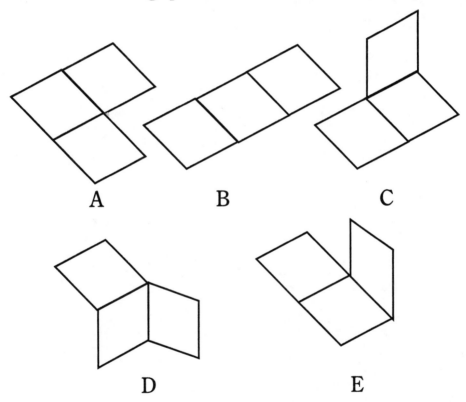

A   B   C

D   E

(Solution 119)

The
Solutions

(Solutions are presented out of numerical sequence
so that reading the answer to one puzzle will not inadvertently
reveal the answer to the next.)

1 Find a Word

Investigation

(Puzzle 41)

2 Magic "34"

7	2	9	16
13	12	3	6
4	5	14	11
10	15	8	1

(Puzzle 80)

3 Brain Strain

7	+	5	−	3	=	9
+		+		+		×
7	+	3	−	6	=	4
−		÷		−		÷
8	+	4	−	6	=	6
=		=		=		=
6	÷	2	+	3	=	6

(Puzzle 121)

4 "X" Puzzle

Xiphoid, Xylene, Xylem, Xyloid, Dexter, Lynx, Rex, Lax, Ax, Axe, Hex, Exact, Text, Tax, Taxes, Exam, Sex, Ox, Pix, Nix, Pyx, Tux.

(Puzzle 1)

5 Synonym Circles

Siblings
Children

(Puzzle 42)

6 Square Numbers

Across: 4489, 1681, 2916, 9604, 6241, 3025, 5776, 3136
Down: 4356, 1764, 9801, 2304, 5929, 1444, 3136, 2209

(Puzzle 81)

7 Circle

Less than 25%:

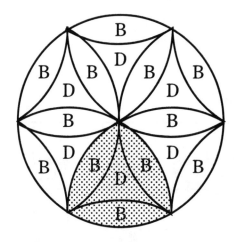

(Puzzle 122)

8 Warehouse

C:

A	8×	C	7×
B	4×	D	6×

Starting at A each mile move towards B increases mileage per week by 8, but decreases it by 17: 4 + 7 + 6 = 17.

From B to C we get + (8 + 4) – (7 + 6) – 1, so the number is still going down.

After C we get + (8 + 4 + 7) – 6, so it goes up. Therefore C is best.

(Puzzle 2)

9 Grid

2C.

(Puzzle 43)

10 Middle Letters

Fuss-budget
Miserly
Fuzzy-wuzzy
Frangipani
Flunkeydom
Dust-jacket
Farfetched
Eisteddfod
Daisy-chain
Dapple-gray

(Puzzle 82)

11 Alphabet Crossword

(Puzzle 3)

12 "E" Frame

	DOWN 1	2	3	4	5	6	7	8	
A C R O S S 1	R	L	S	P	T	L	D	T	DESERT
2	Y	P	L	S	D	T	L	P	STEPPED
3	B	B	B	P	D	H	W	L	WEBBED
4	K	J	R	N	S	N	N	T	JENNET
5	L	D	N	P	L	S	N	S	ENDLESS
6	N	R	L	K	R	T	N	B	KENNEL
7	W	R	C	R	F	B	D	M	DEFER
8	N	T	H	T	M	R	F	M	ENTER
	WEEKLY	TREBLE	LECHER	PEPPER	MEREST	BETHEL	FENNEL	EMBLEM	

(Puzzle 123)

13 Chairs

$2 \times 7!$
$= 2 \times 7 \times 6 \times 5 \times 4 \times 3 \times 2 \times 1$
$= 10080$

(Puzzle 44)

14 Sequence

B. The rectangle moves clockwise through 45° each time, as does the square.

(Puzzle 83)

15 Symbols

D.

(Puzzle 124)

16 Reverse Anagram

Tambourine

(Puzzle 4)

17 Double Bigrams

Hippopotamus, Philology, Sereneness, Convivial, Balalaika, Entities, Imbibing, Stowaway, Prototype, Rhododendron, Uninitiated, Training, Sordidity, Catatonic.

(Puzzle 45)

18 Baby

7.2 lbs:
$12.96 \div 1.8 = 7.2$

(Puzzle 84)

19 Add a Letter

A:
Cashew
Sumach
Orange
Orache
Sesame

(Puzzle 125)

20 Number

The first two numbers in each line or column are divided by either 4 or 3, whichever is possible, and the quotients added together to produce the third number, i.e., $(8 \div 4) + (12 \div 3) = 6$. Thus the missing number is 4.

(Puzzle 46)

21 No Blanks

S	C	A	L	A	R	▓	R	E	M	A	N	D
E	▓	R	I	C	E	P	A	P	E	R	▓	I
M	I	T	T	E	N	▓	M	E	T	R	E	S
I	▓	I	▓	R	E	V	U	E	▓	I	▓	I
C	A	S	T	▓	W	A	S	▓	O	V	E	N
O	▓	T	E	G	▓	T	▓	H	O	E	▓	V
N	▓	▓	N	E	W	▓	F	E	Z	▓	▓	E
D	▓	C	O	T	▓	M	▓	N	E	T	▓	S
U	P	O	N	▓	L	A	C	▓	S	O	F	T
C	▓	V	▓	D	O	N	O	R	▓	I	▓	M
T	R	E	P	A	N	▓	M	E	A	L	I	E
O	▓	R	E	M	E	D	I	A	T	E	▓	N
R	O	T	T	E	R	▓	C	R	E	D	I	T

(Puzzle 5)

22 Names

They all end the names of COUNTRIES:
> AfghaniSTAN — PakiSTAN
> ArgenTINA
> DenMARK
> JorDAN — SuDAN

(Puzzle 85)

23 Fair Play

13.5 minutes: $\dfrac{15 \times 36}{40}$

(Puzzle 6)

24 *Directional Crossword*

¹M	⁵E	V	A	W	E	D	I	⁴T
¹⁰E	I	D	¹³N	E	P	¹²O	N	⁷S
P	L	S	U	E	C	E	T	S
I	¹⁷E	B	G	C	L	E	¹⁵O	U
T	R	O	A	U	A	L	E	C
H	¹⁸R	B	B	M	I	T	¹⁴Y	S
E	O	R	E	¹⁶O	A	D	E	I
¹¹T	U	⁸R	O	B	O	⁹T	E	⁶D
³T	N	A	R	O	D	O	E	²D

1. Misguided
2. Deodorant
3. Turbulent
4. Tidewave
5. Educated
6. Discuss
7. Steamer
8. Robot
9. Tamable

10. Epithet
11. Tobacco
12. Open
13. Nelly
14. Yeo
15. Olio
16. Oboe
17. Err

(Puzzle 126)

25 **Matrix**

G. Looking both across and down, lines which are common in the first two squares are not carried forward to the third square.

(Puzzle 47)

26 Do-it-Yourself Crossword

I	L	L	U	S	T	R	A	T	E	D
N		A		O		O		O		U
T	U	T	O	R		B	A	T	O	N
E		H		T	H	E				E
R	U	E		S	I	S	T	E	R	S
		R		K			M			
D	E	S	I	R	E	D		B	A	R
O				A	R	E		A		I
L	I	K	E	N		B	U	R	N	T
T		E		E		U		G		E
S	U	G	G	E	S	T	I	O	N	S

(Puzzle 86)

27 Anagrammed Synonyms

1. TOO – BESIDES
2. WEAK – ENERVATED
3. HIND – POSTERIOR
4. KISS – OSCULATE
5. POST – PALISADE
6. EBB – RETREAT
7. WHET – STIMULATE
8. ACT – ORDINANCE
9. EAT – INGEST
10. VICE – WEAKNESS

(Puzzle 7)

28 Quartering a Square

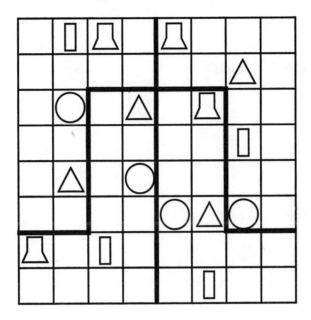

(Puzzle 127)

29 Anagrammed Magic Square

S	C	A	R	F
C	A	T	E	R
A	T	O	N	E
R	E	N	T	S
F	R	E	S	H

(Puzzle 48)

30 Comparison

C.

(Puzzle 87)

31 Concentration

F.

(Puzzle 128)

32 1984

5:

```
    780
    941
 +  263
   1984
```

(Puzzle 8)

33 Stations

56:
8×7

(Puzzle 49)

34 The Puzzling Puzzle

Mystery, Conundrum, Enigma, Paradox, Problem, Bewilderment.

(Puzzle 88)

35 Polling Day

Add 23,968 + 1026 + 2822 + 6428 = 34,244.
Divide by four = 8561.
8561 is the number of votes received by the successful candidate. The second received 7535 (8561 – 1026), the third 5739 (8561 – 2822), and fourth 2133 (8561 – 6428).

(Puzzle 129)

36 Round the Hexagons

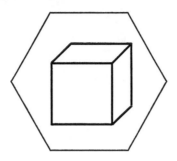

Working from top to bottom, every third hexagon contains the contents of the two previous hexagons.

(Puzzle 9)

37 Hexagram

Salmon, Grilse, Burbot, Groper, Blenny, Plaice.
Key = BARBEL

(Puzzle 50)

38 Bath

This is solved by reciprocals in the formula $(a^{-1} + b^{-1} - c^{-1})^{-1}$
$= (8^{-1} + 10^{-1} - 5^{-1})^{-1}$, i.e., $8^{-1} = \frac{1}{8}$
$= (0.125 + 0.1 - 0.2)^{-1} = 0.025^{-1}$
$= \frac{1}{0.025} = 40$ minutes

(Puzzle 89)

39 Alternatives

1. (c)   5. (a)
2. (a)   6. (a)
3. (a)   7. (a)
4. (b)   8. (a)

(Puzzle 130)

40 Hexagon

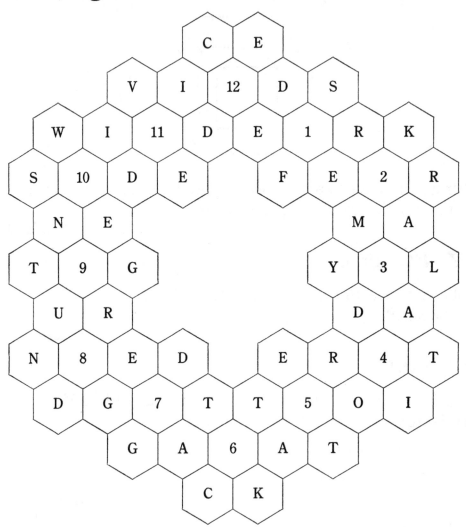

41 Homonym

You – Ewe

(Puzzle 51)

42 Ten-Digit Number

2100010006

(Puzzle 131)

43 Circles

The contents of the middle circle are determined by the contents of the four circles surrounding it. Only when the same circle appears in the same position in three (and only three) of the surrounding circles is it carried forward to the middle circle.

(Puzzle 90)

44 Circles

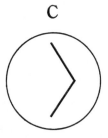

Each pair of circles produces the circle above by carrying forward only the similar elements.

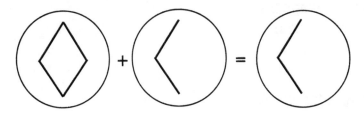

(Puzzle 11)

45 Comparison

C.

(Puzzle 132)

46 Circles

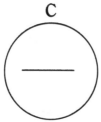

Each pair of circles produces the circle above by carrying forward only the similar elements.

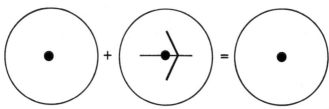

(Puzzle 52)

47 Fish

1. Proper – Groper
2. Cattle – Cuttle
3. Gunner – Gunnel
4. Nipper – Kipper
5. Duffer – Puffer
6. Dudgeon – Gudgeon
7. Sapper – Wapper
8. Dream – Bream
9. Bullet – Mullet

(Puzzle 91)

48 Pentagram

Civet
Camel
Panda   Key = COATI
Stoat
Tapir

(Puzzle 53)

49 Work it Out

C. The final figure in each line is determined by the number of sides in each figure as follows:

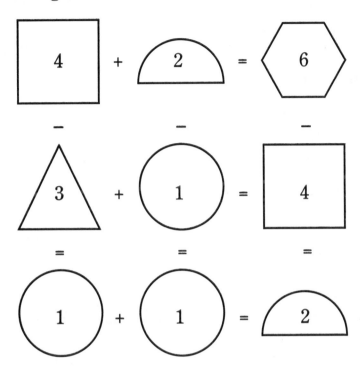

(Puzzle 133)

50 Target Crossword

- Noggin
- Possum
- Sexton
- Seesaw
- Eyelid
- Picnic
- Poseur
- Shandy
- Lineal
- Shaman
- Rouble
- Parody
- Sconce
- Rights
- Piazza
- Gingko

(Puzzle 12)

51 Something in Common

They are all names of SHIPS or BOATS:
Packet, Punt, Barge, Liner, Smack, Tramp, Tender, Trader

(Puzzle 54)

52 Odd One Out

G:
B is the same as E
A is the same as D
C is the same as F

(Puzzle 92)

53 Found in the USA

1. The Empire State Building
2. The Grand Canyon
3. Great Salt Lake
4. Rocky Mountains
5. Lake Michigan
6. The White House

(Puzzle 134)

54 Sequence

1021:
Allocate the numbers 1–26 to the alphabet, i.e., A=1, B=2,
C=3, etc.
The numbers are formed by the first two letters of the months of
the year starting with January: J(10), A(1) = 101.
The seventh month is, therefore July: J(10), U(21) = 1021.

(Puzzle 13)

55 Octagons

D. The shield twists around three sides of the octagon each time.
The arrow moves from top to bottom of the shield in turn and
points to the outside, then the inside, of the shield in turn.

(Puzzle 55)

56 Odd One Out

E:
A is the same as C
B is the same as G
D is the same as F

(Puzzle 135)

57 Nursery Rhyme Crossword

M	A	J	E	S	T	Y
E		E		C		I
R	E	S	T	O	R	E
I		T		O		L
T	R	E	A	T	E	D
E		R		E		E
D	E	S	I	R	E	D

(Puzzle 93)

58 No Repeat Letters

Speculator

(Puzzle 14)

59 Cards

$52p_4 = 52 \times 51 \times 50 \times 49$

$= 6,497,400$

(Puzzle 56)

60 Network

Representative

(Puzzle 94)

61 Word Circle

Starch, Cheese, Senate, Tenure, Resume, Mettle, Legacy, Cypher, Ermine, Nebula, Lavish, Shelve, Vendor, Origin, Infest.

(Puzzle 15)

62 Anagram Theme

The theme is COUNTRIES:

Nigeria	Gain	Ire
Finland	Flan	Din
Austria	Aura	Sit
Sweden	Sew	End
Argentina	Grain	Neat
Algeria	Rail	Age
Hungary	Rung	Hay

(Puzzle 136)

63 Number Logic

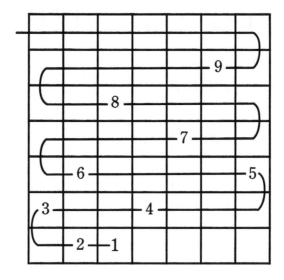

Start at the top left-hand corner and work in the direction indicated, counting the same number of squares as the next number each time.

(Puzzle 57)

64 Find Another Word

LONG. All words can be prefixed with FUR to form another word: Furbelow, Furore, Furrower, Furlong.

(Puzzle 95)

65 Nines

3	8	5	2
8	7	9	3
6	6	5	1
1	6	8	3

(Puzzle 137)

66 Missing Square

D. The number of sides in the figures in each horizontal, vertical and corner-to-corner line add up to 15.

(Puzzle 16)

67 Sequence

B. The figure alternates:

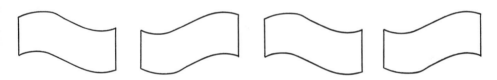

The lines are first introduced into the circles on the left, one at a time in rotation, and then transfer to the circle on the right at the next stage.

(Puzzle 58)

68 Missing Letters

1. Anatomist
2. Stuntman
3. Boatswain
4. Rivetter
5. Japanner
6. Dietician
7. Usherette
8. Violinist
9. Mercenary
10. Gasfitter

(Puzzle 138)

69 Connections

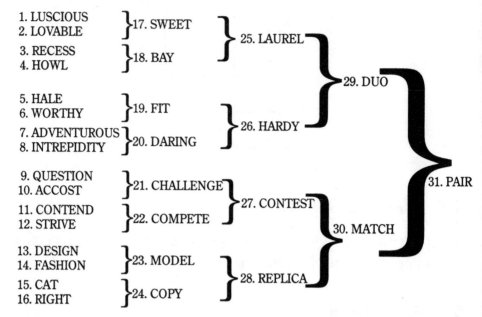

(Puzzle 96)

70 Logic

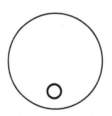

Carrying forward only similar symbols:

Row 1	A added to B = C
Row 2	A added to B = C
Row 3	A added to B = C
Column A	1 added to 2 = 3
Column B	1 added to 2 = 3
Column C	1 added to 2 = 3

(Puzzle 17)

71 Word Power

1.   Pussyfoot
2.   Musketeer
3.   Cantaloup
4.   Debaucher
5.   Flagstone
6.   Marijuana
7.   Recumbent
8.   Objection
9.   Gallivant

(Puzzle 59)

72 Ending

PER:
Hamper
Pamper
Hopper
Whimper
Supper
Slipper

(Puzzle 97)

73 Sequence

E. The rectangle and diamond form alternate sequences. First
the rectangle turns through 90°, then the diamond does the
same.

(Puzzle 139)

74 Old Age

88:
$100 - (4 \times 10) = 60$
$60 + (4 \times 7) = 88$

(Puzzle 19)

75 Logic

Carrying forward only similar symbols:

Row 1	A added to B = C
Row 2	A added to B = C
Row 3	A added to B = C
Column A	1 added to 2 = 3
Column B	1 added to 2 = 3
Column C	1 added to 2 = 3

(Puzzle 60)

76 Arrows

F:

The arrow moves 45° clockwise each time.

The arrow head alternates black/striped.

The arrow body alternates striped/black.

The ellipse rotates 45° each time and moves from bottom to top, etc., of arrow.

The circle moves from top to bottom, etc., of arrow and black and white segments alternate.

(Puzzle 98)

77 Niners

Across	Down	Diagonal
1. Announcer	1. Anarchist	1. Accusable
4. Crossover	2. Unreserve	3. Renascent
5. Teakettle	3. Recursive	

(Puzzle 140)

78 Pyramid

Unsportsmanlike

(Puzzle 61)

79 Sequence

D:

D	E F G H	I	(4)
I	J K L M N	O	(5)
O	P Q R S T U	V	(6)
V	W X Y Z A B C	D	(7)

(Puzzle 18)

80 Sequence

Trudy: The names can all be made from the days of the week starting SuNDAY (ANDY). Trudy can be produced from SaTURDaY.

(Puzzle 62)

81 Safe

Lynx

(Puzzle 99)

82 Safe

3W.

(Puzzle 141)

83 Word Search

DRINKS:
Chartreuse, Grenadine, Cappuccino, Cointreau, Muscadine, Orangeade, Martini, Arrack, Alcohol, Lager, Grog, Gimlet, Nog, Ale, Rosé, Cha, Hock, Tea, Fizz, Rye.

(Puzzle 20)

84 Clueless Crossword

P	L	U	M	B	E	R
L		P		U		E
A	P	P	A	R	E	L
T		E		S		I
E	R	R	A	T	I	C

(Puzzle 63)

85 Complete the Calculation

$6^3 \div 36 = 6$

(Puzzle 100)

86 Song

All around the mulberry bush,
The monkey chased the weasel,
The monkey thought it was such fun –
Pop goes the weasel!

(Puzzle 142)

87 Letters Sequence

TH. They are the last two letters of each planet in reverse order
from the Sun:
PluTO, NeptuNE, UranUS, SatuRN, JupitER, MaRS, EarTH.

(Puzzle 21)

88 Three Triangles

(Puzzle 64)

89 Grid

2A.

(Puzzle 101)

90 Pyramid Word

L, Pi, Gun, Deer, Drive.
15-letter word: UNDERPRIVILEGED

(Puzzle 143)

91 Bracket Word

Altogether

(Puzzle 22)

92 No Neighbors

Transmogrification

(Puzzle 103)

93 Alternative Crossword

F	R	O	M		A	I	R	S
L		R	U	M	P	S		P
I	T		D	I	E		M	E
P	I	T		N		R	O	D
	D	E	C	I	D	E	D	
H	E	N		M		D	E	W
U	S		N	U	B		S	O
N		T	I	M	E	D		R
T	O	O	L		G	O	O	D

(Puzzle 65)

94 Middle Word

1. Joss
2. Jib
3. Girandole
4. Glutton
5. Farce
6. Fawn
7. Ferret
8. Fitch
9. Poppet
10. Shard

(Puzzle 144)

95 Odd One Out

B:
A is the same as D with Black and White reversed.
C is the same as E with Black and White reversed.

(Puzzle 23)

96 Circles

E:

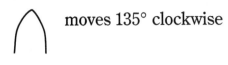 moves 135° clockwise

 moves 180°

moves 90°

moves 135°

(Puzzle 66)

97 Cross-Alphabet

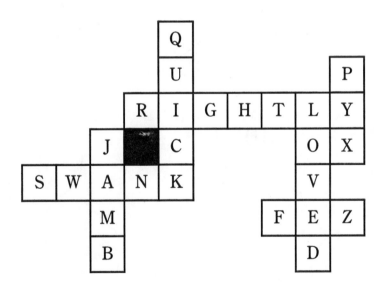

(Puzzle 145)

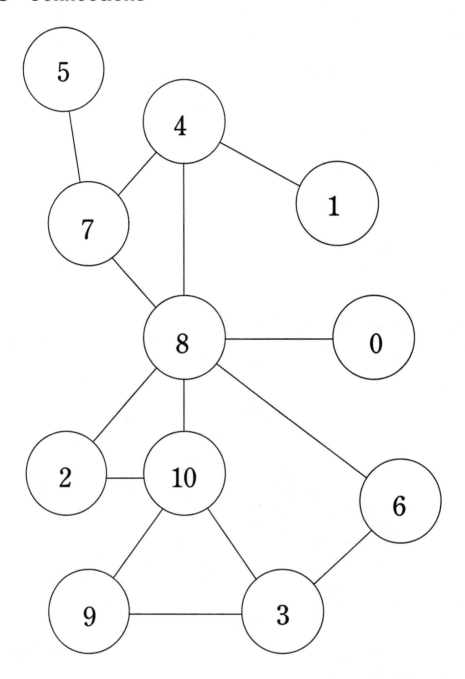

(Puzzle 102)

99 Word Power

Eldrich
Ukase
Refection
Extirpate
Kohl
Amain
Impecunious
Vicarious
Esculent
Gerund
Odalisk
Termagant
Inanition
Tolu
"Eureka! I've got it." – *Archimedes*

(Puzzle 24)

100 Square Roots

No.
Square these end digits and note last digit: 0 1 2 3 4 5 6 7 8 9
Last digit of squares: 0 1 4 9 6 5 6 9 4 1
No number ending in 2, 3, 7, or 8 can have a square root of integers only.

(Puzzle 67)

101 Missing Links

2798 – 2646 – 1196
4389 – 3827 – 1026
4051 – 2040 – 800
$27 \times 98 = 2646$, $26 \times 46 = 1196$

(Puzzle 104)

102   Number Sequence

$$50746$$
$$1 \times 9 - 1 = 8$$
$$8 \times 9 - 2 = 70$$
$$70 \times 9 - 3 = 627$$
$$627 \times 9 - 4 = 5639$$
$$5639 \times 9 - 5 = 50746$$

(Puzzle 146)

103   Greek Cross to Square Puzzle

The lines AB and CD are drawn from the center of their respective sides of the Greek cross.

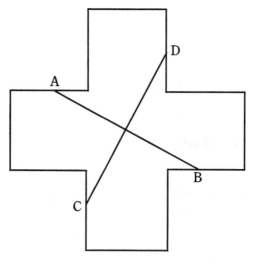

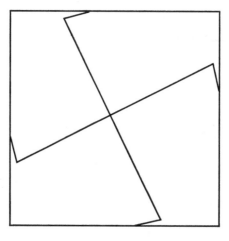

(Puzzle 25)

104 Wine

	hours	reciprocal	decimal
Man	2.5	$1/2.5$	.400
Wife	1.5	$1/1.5$	.667
		Add	1.067

Take reciprocal

$1/1.067 = .9375$ hrs.

$= .9375 \times 60$

$= 56.25$ minutes.

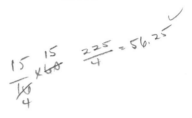

(Puzzle 68)

105 Multiple Magic

13	12	63	3	61	73	59	80	5
81	26	71	28	57	30	55	20	1
78	68	35	60	29	50	31	14	4
6	24	36	40	45	38	46	58	76
75	17	49	39	41	43	33	65	7
8	18	34	44	37	42	48	64	74
15	72	51	22	53	32	47	10	67
16	62	11	54	25	52	27	56	66
77	70	19	79	21	9	23	2	69

(Puzzle 147)

106 Occupations

Ploughman
Professor
Major-domo
Puppeteer
Harpooner
Geologist
Osteopath
Zookeeper
Ropemaker
Gondolier
Herbalist
Hypnotist

(Puzzle 105)

107 Appropriate Anagrams

Dead Respire Again
Is Lit For Seamen
Causes Sin
Is No Meal
Sit Not At Ale Bars
A Stew Sir
Apt Is The Cure
No Hat, A Smile
Noted Miscalculations
Faces One At The End

(Puzzle 26)

108 Alternative Crossword

S	W	A	G	E
H	A	R	E	M
O	V	O	L	O
R	E	M	I	T
T	R	A	D	E

(Puzzle 69)

109 Sea Level

8.7 miles:
The formula is   Height = $\dfrac{2n^2}{3}$ feet

(where n = distance in miles)

$\therefore\ 50 = \dfrac{2n^2}{3}$

$150 = 2n^2$

$75 = n^2$

$n = \sqrt{75}$

$n = 8.7$ miles

(Puzzle 106)

110 Three squares

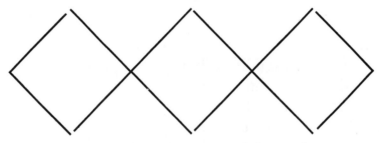

Sorry if this was a bit sneaky, but we didn't say that you couldn't break the matches.

(Puzzle 148)

111 Jumble

Vaccination
Ventilation
Venturesome
Viceroyship
Versatility
Vermiculate
Vicariously
Vexatiously

(Puzzle 27)

112 Anagrammed Phrases

1. Let sleeping dogs lie
2. To give up the ghost
3. To beg the question
4. A fly on the wall
5. Play fast and loose

(Puzzle 70)

113 Logic

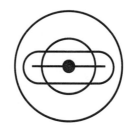

Carrying forward only similar symbols:

Row 1	A added to B = C
Row 2	A added to B = C
Row 3	A added to B = C
Column A	1 added to 2 = 3
Column B	1 added to 2 = 3
Column C	1 added to 2 = 3

(Puzzle 107)

114 Four Integers

A = 9
B = 6
C = 3
D = 1
CABA = 3969
DCBA = 1369
DACB = 1936

(Puzzle 28)

115 Plan in Works

1. To cut it fine
2. Win hands down
3. Look here
4. Dull as ditch water
5. Facts of life
6. Ball of fire
7. To lick the dust
8. See stars
9. Yum yum
10. Woe is me
11. Not to say
12. To try out

(Puzzle 149)

116 Symbols

A.

(Puzzle 29)

117 Work it Out

63: $\dfrac{15 \times 3 \times 7}{5}$

Likewise: $\dfrac{4 \times 3 \times 8}{6} = 16$

$\dfrac{9 \times 12 \times 2}{9} = 24$

(Puzzle 71)

118 Cheeses

63 moves $(2^6 - 1)$

(Puzzle 30)

119 Logical Movement

B. There are three components:

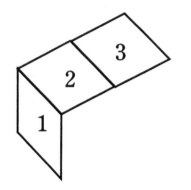

All pieces are laid flat.
Pieces 2 and 3 never move.
Piece 1 moves by rotating
counterclockwise and clamping
itself onto the next available
side.

Thus option 2:

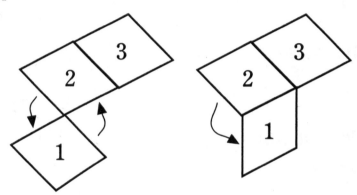

(Puzzle 160)

120 Quotation

"Anyone who thinks that there is a safety in numbers has not
looked at the stock market pages." – *Irene Peter*

(Puzzle 108)

121 Comparison

A.

(Puzzle 34)

122 Cryptogram

Write we know is written right, when we see it written write;
But when we see it written wright, we know 'tis not then written
 right;
For write to have it written right, must not be written right nor
 wright;
Nor yet should it be written rite, but write – for so 'tis written
 right.

(Puzzle 72)

123 Dominoes

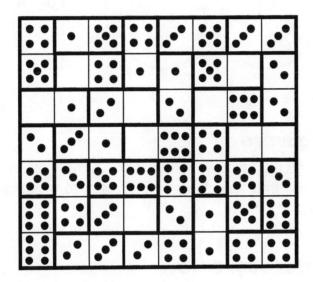

(Puzzle 109)

124 The Gallopers

ANNOYING (Exasperating), LAG (Delay)

LING (Heather), OBLONG (Rectangular)

PRIG (Puritan), EVERLASTING (Imperishable)

ROUSING (Stimulating), SPRING (Fountainhead)

(Puzzle 31)

125 Circles

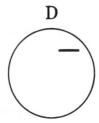

Each pair of circles produces the circle above by carrying forward only the similar elements.

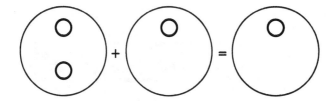

(Puzzle 159)

126 Sequence

C. Break them into groups of four. They tumble over one at a time from the right, and change from black to white one at a time from the left.

(Puzzle 73)

127 Letter Sequence

R. They are all alternate letters in:

       ThE uNiTeD sTaTeS oF aMeRica

(Puzzle 110)

128 Pyramid Quotation

O, we, key, huge, shout, thieve, sequins, petition, dalmation

(Puzzle 158)

129 Analogy

C. The figure is inverted and the inverted figure placed on top on the original figure touching the top and bottom of it. The external parts in the figure created are shaded.

(Puzzle 32)

130 Sequence

REEF:

RAY (ON E) PAULE (T WO) R (TH REE) F

(Puzzle 74)

131 Odd One Out

Open.

All other words are made up from the initials of the numbers 1–10 : OTTFFSSENT.

(Puzzle 111)

132 Missing Number

1. The link is in each horizontal line:

$$7 = \frac{4 + 6 + 11}{3}$$

$$8 = \frac{8 + 1 + 15}{3}$$

$$5 = \frac{6 + 8 + 1}{3}$$

(Puzzle 157)

133 Birds

Crested	Grebe
Carrier	Pigeon
Stormy	Petrel
Snow	Goose
Muscovy	Duck
Tawny	Owl
Night	Hawk
Water	Ousel
Turtle	Dove
House	Martin
Willow	Warbler
Black	Cockatoo

Odd word: PEACOCK

(Puzzle 33)

134 Missing Number

4:
The number inside the octagon is produced by doing the opposite calculation to that indicated immediately above.

i.e.

$7 + 3$ ∴ actual calculation $7 - 3 = 4$

3×3 ∴ actual calculation $3 \div 3 = 1$

$3 - 2$ ∴ actual calculation $3 + 2 = 5$

$2 - 7$ ∴ actual calculation $2 + 7 = 9$

(Puzzle 112)

135 Knight

We find it hard to believe that other people's thoughts are as silly as our own, but they probably are.

(Puzzle 35)

136 Threes

They are all names of groups:

Pack
{ Hyenas
Wolves
Cigarettes

Rookery
{ Penguins
Rooks
Seals

Drove
{ Pigs
Swine
Oxen

Nest
{ Machine Guns
Wasps
Mice

Pod
{ Peas
Whales
Hippopotamuses

Troop
{ Scouts
Baboons
Actors

(Puzzle 75)

137 Honeycomb

ANIMALS:

Moose	Coyote	Coypu
Pup	Puppy	Sore
Mice	Possum	Teg
Musk	Cob	Bat
Nag	Tat	Moco
Stag		

(Puzzle 156)

138 Series

To get from one term to the next term, multiply by 3,
e.g., $6 \times 3 = 18$.
We require the 10th term, i.e., 6×3^9:
$= 6 \times 19683$
$= 118098$

(Puzzle 36)

139 Common

They all begin with things associated with water but with letters reversed.

1. Bib   5. Gar

2. Carp   6. Tide

3. Dab   7. Newt

4. Crab   8. Orca

(Puzzle 76)

140 Middle Words

1. By   5. Me   9. He

2. King   6. Ring   10. Cap

3. Fish   7. Ate

4. Wood   8. Lock

(Puzzle 113)

141 1-2-3

1113213211:
Each line describes the number above it.
For example, 1221 would be:
One 1, Two 2, One 1, etc.

(Puzzle 155)

142 Division

YOUNGSTER

N	T	G	E	O	O
N	U	Y	N	S	S
Y	U	R	R	Y	E
R	G	O	S	U	G
E	Y	S	O	T	U
T	G	E	T	R	N

(Puzzle 37)

143 Scales

13.5 grams:
$9 \times 6 = 4 \times 13.5$

(Puzzle 77)

144 Track Word

Instantaneously

(Puzzle 114)

145 Magic Square

G	R	A	N	T
R	I	G	O	R
A	G	O	N	Y
N	O	N	E	S
T	R	Y	S	T

(Puzzle 154)

146 Three Animals

Panther, Antelope, Llama

(Puzzle 38)

147 Symbols

A.

(Puzzle 78)

148 Quotation

"The minute you read something you can't understand, you can almost be sure it was drawn up by a lawyer." – *Will Rogers*

(Puzzle 115)

149 Brackets

1. Proof
2. Light
3. Play
4. Whip
5. Lock

6. Over
7. Fire
8. Fly
9. Land
10. Point

(Puzzle 153)

150 Number

14:

$(7 \times 2) + 7 - 7 = 14$

(Puzzle 152)

151   Equilateral Triangle

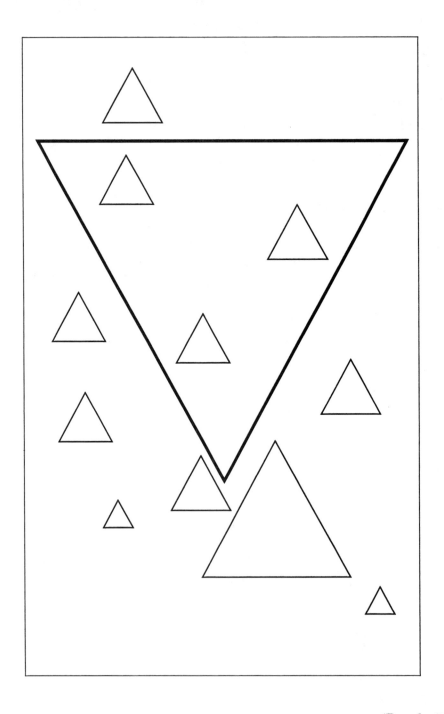

(Puzzle 39)

152 Eponyms

1. Leotard – after Jules Léotard
2. Draconian – after Draco
3. Maverick – after Samual Maverick
4. Cardigan – after the Earl of Cardigan
5. Platonic – after Plato
6. Lucullan – after Lucius Licinius Lucullus
7. Martinet – after Jean Martinet
8. Dunce – after John Duns Scotus
9. Mesmerize – after Franz Anton Mesmer
10. Machiavellian – after Nicolò Machiavelli

(Puzzle 79)

153 Circles

B:

moves 135°
clockwise

moves 90°
counterclockwise

moves 180°

moves 90°
clockwise

(Puzzle 116)

154 Trios

1. Adjustment	Variation	Alteration
2. Cessation	Conclusion	Resolution
3. Divine	Revered	Venerable
4. Graceful	Charming	Elegant
5. Deceitful	Imitation	Counterfeit
6. Swivel	Intertwine	Weave

(Puzzle 151)

155 Odd One Out

D:
A is the same as F
B is the same as E
C is the same as G

(Puzzle 150)

156 Quotation

"I have made it a rule never to smoke more than one cigar at a time." – *Mark Twain*

(Puzzle 117)

157 Directional Numbers

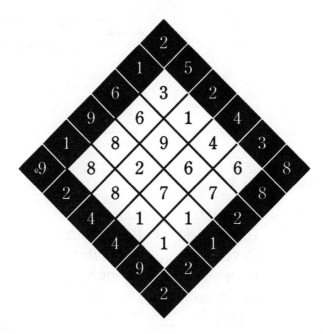

(Puzzle 40)

158 The Hexagonal Pyramid

The content of each hexagon is made up by merging the contents of the two hexagons directly below, with the exception that where two identical lines appear they are not carried forward.

(Puzzle 119)

159 Synchronized Synonyms

Towering, Gigantic
Dextrous, Polished
Director, Governor
Isolated, Solitary
Swindler, Deceiver
Calendar, Schedule
Disallow, Preclude
Latitude, Wideness

(Puzzle 120)

160 Spots

The formula is by Leo Moser: $n + \binom{n}{4} \; \binom{n-1}{2}$

Written in full: $\dfrac{n^4 - 6n^3 + 23n^2 - 18n + 24}{24}$

Amazingly the answer is not 32. It is as follows:

Spots	Regions	Spots	Regions
1	1	7	57
2	2	8	99
3	4	9	163
4	8	10	256
5	16	11	386
6	31		

Answers can be obtained by a cut from Pascal's triangle.

```
                1
              1   1
            1   2   1
          1   3   3   1
        1   4   6   4   1
      1   5   10  10  5 / 1
    1   6   15  20  15/ 6   1
  1   7   21  35  35/ 21  7   1
```

(Puzzle 118)

154